# Assisting Numeracy

## A handbook for classroom assistants

by Ruth Aplin

This book is a joint venture between BEAM;
The National Numeracy Project; and
the London Borough of Tower Hamlets.

Cover illustration by Emma Whiting
Other illustrations by Anna de Polnay except p50 by Andy Martin
Photographs © Sally Greenhill except those on pp17 (top), 27 and 93 © Simon Spain

British Library Cataloguing-in-Publication Data
A catalogue record for this book is available from the British Library.

ISBN 18 74099 72 3

Designed and typeset by Billie Old
Edited by Ros Elphinstone, Sheila Ebbutt and Fran Mosley
Printed by Five Castles Press Ltd, Duke Street, Ipswich, IP3 0AG

# Contents

# Introduction

" You provide me with another mind as well as another pair of hands. "

*A class teacher to her assistant*

This book is for learning support assistants — that is, classroom assistants — and the teachers they work with. It looks at the ways in which mathematics is taught in schools today, and provides practical support in the form of mathematical games and activities.

The introduction that follows is divided into two parts. The first part is for the assistant. The second part is for the teacher who works with the assistant, or is involved in their training.

# To the assistant

## Numeracy

Mathematics is a difficult subject to learn. It is very abstract, and it takes years to grasp the complex ideas involved. Children need all the help they can get to gain a real understanding of it.

Nowadays there is a lot of talk about 'numeracy' and teaching children to be 'numerate'. A numerate child has more than just a good knowledge of numbers. He or she is able to apply this knowledge of numbers in real-life situations. We want to help children grow up and thrive in the modern world. To do so they need to be able to use numbers in all sorts of ways and in every kind of situation.

## A child at primary school who is numerate:

- has a sense of the size of a number

- knows where numbers fit in the number system

- knows by heart the times tables and other number facts

- uses what she knows by heart to work things out in her head

- uses a range of methods of calculating, in his head and on paper

- uses a calculator when she really needs to

- makes sense of number problems and knows how to solve them

- checks his answers

- knows whether her answer is reasonable

- talks about how he works things out

- explains her mathematical ideas

I don't know the answer to that. How can I find out?

## What you can do

All children could become numerate, but they need help to get there. There are various ways in which you can help children to get better at working with numbers.

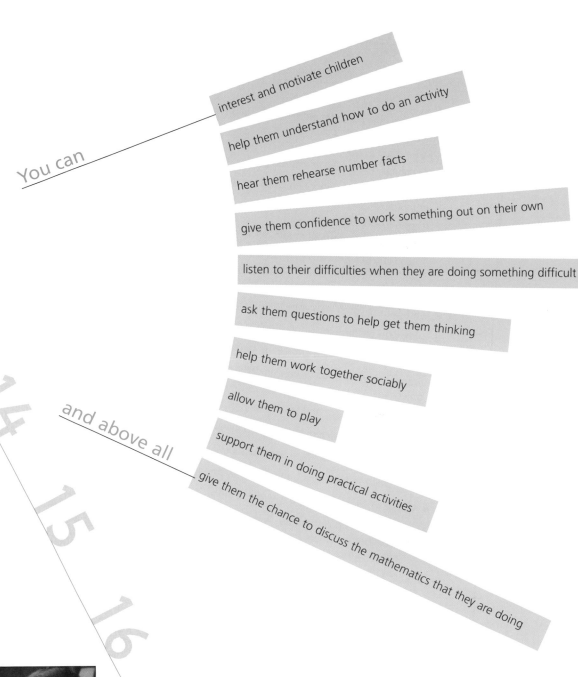

You can

- interest and motivate children
- help them understand how to do an activity
- hear them rehearse number facts
- give them confidence to work something out on their own
- listen to their difficulties when they are doing something difficult
- ask them questions to help get them thinking
- help them work together sociably
- allow them to play

and above all

- support them in doing practical activities
- give them the chance to discuss the mathematics that they are doing

**To the assistant**

# The job you do

The role of the classroom assistant varies from school to school, but there are many jobs that all assistants will have in common. You will probably recognise many of the jobs listed below as things you have been asked to do in the past, or still do now.

## JOB DESCRIPTION FOR A TEACHING ASSISTANT

**JOB PURPOSE:**
To assist the class teacher with the education, supervision and welfare of all the children in the class.

**DUTIES**
The particular responsibilities of the post holder will be to:

- work with small groups of children (up to six) under the teacher's supervision, for example:
  - hearing children read
  - assisting children with meanings of words, spelling, handwriting, presentation
  - assisting children when carrying out practical science or mathematics tasks, using equipment
  - supervising the playing of educational games
- work with children with varying degrees of learning difficulties
- work with children for whom English is an additional language
- assist in the long- and short-term planning of work with children
- prepare work and activities with children in advance, in accordance with the objectives set by the teacher
- attend INSET days and staff meetings
- be familiar with school policies and schemes of work
- help children in individual and collaborative study skills
- give children feedback on their achievements and progress
- discuss children's progress with teachers
- operate AVA equipment as required, for example, photocopier, laminator
  - make books, labels, signs, and undertake any other practical tasks to maintain a good standard in classroom appearance
- help ensure that children adhere to the school's behaviour policy
- meet children's physical needs, while encouraging independence, for example:
  - help children to change for PE lessons or swimming
  - clean and reassure children after accidental soiling of clothes
- help ensure that a high standard of health and safety is maintained at all times
- administer First Aid as needed and accompany sick or injured children home
- organise and supervise children in the playground
- accompany teachers and pupils on educational visits

There may be some things on this list for which you are not currently responsible, but would like to try your hand at. If so, you could show the list to your headteacher, or whoever is your manager, and ask whether your role might be renegotiated to include these extra responsibilities.

## Supporting children with particular needs

Classroom assistants often help children who have individual educational needs. These may be children with special educational needs, or children with physical disabilities, or children who have difficulties learning at the same rate as others of their age, or children who are learning English as an additional language.

The teacher will plan the mathematics curriculum that these children follow, but children with individual needs often benefit from extra adult attention and intervention. The teacher needs to liaise very closely with you when you are working for long periods with specific children, to make sure that the children are progressing in the way that you and the teacher intend. There is a delicate balance between giving crucial support to children, and finding that they have become dependent on adult attention. Discussing individual children's learning with the teacher is an important part of your role, and the school should organise time for this to happen.

## Planning your work with the teacher

The teacher is responsible for planning the mathematics curriculum of the children. Because you have a close involvement with individual children and their learning, it is important that the teacher includes you early on in these overall plans. You need to know what learning objectives the teacher has planned for the children, so that you can help the children achieve them. You also need to know what learning you should look out for.

This book provides examples of activities that you and the teacher may find useful to build into the children's work programme. There is help with what to look for in children's learning, and at what age children are expected to achieve certain things.

At the back of this book, on page 95, we have provided a feedback sheet. This is intended to help with individual activities, rather than the curriculum as a whole. The teacher fills in the details of the activity and what the children might learn. You then fill in what happens during the activity, and how well the children understood what they did. It is very important to talk to the teacher as well as to fill in the form. In discussion, you can give very valuable information to the teacher that you often wouldn't write down. The feedback sheet gives you something to base the discussion on — it is not intended to replace your meeting with the teacher.

## Assessing children

When you work on mathematics with small groups of children, they will talk to you about their ideas. You can ask children to tell you more about these ideas. You can learn a lot about how they understand mathematics and what they know. This is very useful information for the teacher. It helps you and the teacher plan how to help the children's next activities.

You can also watch children while the teacher is talking with the whole class to see if they are joining in, and to assess how well they take part. You might offer some children quiet help during this time.

To assess children in this way, you and the teacher need to agree what mathematics you both expect them to learn, and what the children might do or say to show they are learning it.

9

# To the teacher

## Classroom assistants in the school

Classroom assistants are an invaluable resource and you need to plan carefully how to use them. As a school you should formulate an agreed policy on how classroom assistants can benefit your children and their learning. You should be clear about what you can reasonably expect the assistants to do and what help and guidance they need. All schools should have a clear job description for classroom assistants and all teachers should know what their own role is. Time must be made for joint planning and feedback sessions.

Part of your school policy should contain guidance for the training of classroom assistants. This book is a useful resource for training. Many of the ideas in the book can be incorporated into specific training objectives. A clear message is the importance of children developing independence in their learning. We have emphasised this by developing the role of the assistant in asking children questions to further their thinking and help them solve problems for themselves. We have looked to classroom assistants to help develop children's learning processes, rather than concentrate on narrow skills and short-term outcomes of activities. This is an area where there is great scope for training. The class teacher has a clear role in providing mentoring support on a one-to-one basis.

## Teaching, learning and planning

Because classroom assistants are such a precious resource, you need to be sure that they share your objectives for the children's mathematical learning, so that you are both working to the same end. It is vital to find time for the pair of you to have discussions early on about overall curriculum planning. It is important to give classroom assistants the opportunity to understand why you want children to experience certain activities and to understand how children learn mathematics, and how this fits into the overall progress and development of children throughout the primary school. It is not always obvious to those not trained as teachers what makes some experiences more significant than others in the classroom. If you don't make it explicit, it will not always be clear what it is you specifically want the children to learn.

The feedback sheet on page 95 offers an opportunity for dialogue with the classroom assistant on a short-term basis. Fill in the details of the activity you have planned with the assistant, and the learning objectives and intended outcomes. The assistant can then record what happens during the activity, and what the children appear to learn. However, written feedback cannot replace in-depth discussions about children's needs and detailed assessment of children's learning.

## Assessing children

Classroom assistants can give you valuable information about children's development in mathematics. In order for them to acquire this information and pass it on to you, they need to know what you intend the children to learn, and what to look for in children's speech and actions to indicate their knowledge and understanding. In this book we offer a repertoire of questions that an assistant can ask during mathematical activities to probe children's thinking. You should encourage the use of this style of questioning, and foster the skills of listening to and remembering key features of children's responses. Make time to observe the assistant working with the children. They may not realise how many skills they have developed, so offer them positive feedback.

You will need to think how best to involve the classroom assistant at the beginning and ending of a mathematics lesson, when you are introducing new mathematical concepts to children, listening to their ideas, involving them in discussions and asking them to join in your conclusions to the lesson. A valuable use of the assistant's time is to focus on particular children and monitor their responses to the discussion. You need to agree beforehand what to look out for — for example, whether particular children appear to engage in the lesson, whether they make any attempt to respond to general questions, any specific responses they make and so on. The assistant can also sit near children who need help and give them quiet and discreet help during these whole class sessions. During a plenary session the assistant can help a particular group feed back to the whole group, perhaps displaying particular skills these children might have, such as specific kinds of finger counting.

## Supporting children with particular needs

Classroom assistants sometimes work with certain children more than others, and sometimes exclusively with individuals with particular educational needs. You should make sure that you and the assistant have planned the work for those children together, and that you are both monitoring what the children are learning. Sometimes it can be useful to ask the assistant to move around the class in a supervisory role while you work with a small group, to make sure that all children benefit from your teaching. In this book we have included some activities for larger groups that can be used by the assistant for this purpose, as well as games and activities suitable for working with small groups. The aim is for you and the assistant to work as a team in the classroom.

11

# Using this book

This book is divided into four sections:

## Introduction

The first part of the introduction is for the learning support assistant — that is, the classroom assistant — to read. The second part is for the teacher or mathematics coordinator.

The introduction looks at current issues in mathematics teaching, and questions the role of classroom assistants in schools today. It suggests ways in which the assistant's role might be made more effective with proper planning and regular feedback sessions. It also offers advice for assistants who work with children with special educational needs or who are learning English as an additional language.

## Basics

The second part of the book identifies the main areas of mathematical learning at primary school level. It guides you through the way in which children learn skills and strategies most effectively. Used along with the 'Useful Information' section at the back of the book, it will help you get a feel for the basics of mathematical thinking. There are also lots of tips on how to help children to grasp these basics — and get a good understanding of how and why we use mathematics.

## Activities

The third section looks at the mathematics in all sorts of ordinary classroom situations: story-telling, songs and rhymes, playing in the home corner or the playground, and on school outings. It offers a range of games and activities to help you make the most of all these situations.

## Useful Information

A comprehensive reference section offering information on:

◆ mathematical equipment

◆ a glossary of mathematical words and their meanings

◆ a list of what children in each school year should be able to achieve in mathematics

◆ further resources that might be of interest to you

# Basics

# Language and Mathematics

" children need to
express their
ideas in order to
understand
fully what they are
doing "

## The importance of talking

Children need to talk about the mathematics they are learning. Talking helps children put their ideas into words. It makes them think about the mathematics they are doing. When they explain, children make their own ideas clearer to themselves. They get used to using new words. They understand things better.

When children talk, they also share ideas. They can learn from each other — and children sometimes disagree with each other about ideas. When they argue and explain, they gain more understanding.

In one school, a group of children were asked to add 6 + 18, and then say how they worked it out. One child explained:

"I didn't know the answer so I turned it round and put 18 in my head and used my fingers to count on 6."

The adult asked her why she turned it round. She said:

"Because when I put the big number first, I have enough fingers left to count on six."

The other children joined in the discussion, talking about how to do calculations that are 'too big'. They offered ideas about always putting the bigger number first, and about looking for numbers that make ten, such as 8 and 2. Some children in the group learned new ideas from this discussion.

Because you work mainly with small groups of children, you can encourage them to talk. You can ask questions and listen to the replies — and make the other children listen too.

15

Unsure about some mathematical terms? Turn to the Glossary on p87.

## The importance of listening

When you listen to children talking about mathematics, you can find out a lot about what they understand. You can get them to think things through carefully by asking them to explain more clearly what they mean. It's better not to say, "That's wrong," but instead to ask, "What do you mean? How did you work it out? Does everyone else agree?"

Sometimes you can listen without saying anything — but instead, make a note of things children say. You can then pick up on these things later and plan with the teacher how to do more work on them. Listening gives you a chance to analyse what children are thinking.

One child did the calculation 45 – 9 in his head. He explained his method in the following way:

"I split the 9 up in my head into 5 and 4. 45 take away 5 leaves 40.
Then 40 take away 4 leaves 36."

Listening to an explanation like this tells you a lot about how much a child understands. This child clearly knows about how numbers work. Other children could learn from his expertise, as well as sharing their own ideas about how to make a calculation easier.

## The importance of asking questions

It is much better to ask children questions than to tell them the answers or give them ways of doing things. By asking questions you get children to think. By telling them the answers or giving them methods you do their thinking for them. It is useful to have in mind a variety of questions to ask children in different mathematical situations. As time goes on, you will find these occur to you automatically.

Let's look at an example of an activity, and see the range of questions you might have in mind for that activity:

'On a number line, put a circle round the multiples of 4.'

The first problem might be that the child does not recognise the word 'multiple'. Instead of explaining straight away, you could find out a bit more about what the child does know:

Does the word 'multiple' remind you of another word?

What about 'multiply'? What does that mean?

"4 8 12 16 20 24 28 32 36 40 44 48"

This may encourage the child to think through what the problem is likely to mean. If not, you will need to explain what a multiple is. You may then need to prompt the child to think more about what to do:

> How could you find out the multiples of 4?

> Now you know what the multiples of 4 are. What do you have to do next?

If the child gets stuck during the activity, you can ask questions to help her carry on:

> Have you ever done anything like it before?

> Can you tell me what you have done so far?

> Would it help if you used counters? Or a hundred grid?

When the child has finished, you can ask her to check her work, even if it is correct:

> Are those all multiples of 4?
> How do you know?

> Would you know if you had made a mistake? How would you know?'

> Shall I put a ring round 25? Is that a multiple of 4? Why not?

For more information about equipment turn to page 82.

**Language and Mathematics**

# Closed and Open questions

You can ask children two different types of question: closed questions and open questions.

## Closed questions

A closed question has an answer that is either right or wrong.

An example is:

> What must I add to 3 to make 10?

There is just one answer:

> 7

You can use closed questions to find out what facts a child knows. This can be useful. For example, sometimes you need to find out if a child knows the answer to a question such as:

'What are three fives?'

## Open questions

An open question is a question that can have several different answers. The answers can all be correct, or else perfectly acceptable in the context.

Examples are:

> What numbers add together to make 10?

> What does that mean?

The first question has several correct answers. The second question doesn't have particular answers in the same way — it's really a way of getting children to explain. You may not understand their explanation, in which case you can say, "I don't understand. Can you try and explain again in a different way?" But it isn't appropriate to say, "That's wrong."

When you use open questions, you encourage children to think things through. When you ask an open question such as:

'What numbers add together to make 10?'

children can think of more than one solution. They can gain ideas and inspiration from each other, and often become interested in patterns of numbers:

3 + 7, 4 + 6, 5 + 5...

2 + 8, 2 + 2 + 6, 2 + 2 + 2 + 4...

$9\frac{1}{2} + \frac{1}{2}$, $8\frac{1}{2} + 1\frac{1}{2}$, $7\frac{1}{2} + 2\frac{1}{2}$...

This is a very good way to stimulate children into thinking about numbers. It gets them thinking much more than if you ask a closed question like "What is 3 + 7?"

> "Open questions can encourage
> children to think more than
> closed ones do"

Here are some useful questions to ask children while they are working on mathematics activities, to get them to think about and explain what they are doing:

'What are you doing? How are you doing it?'

'What do you know so far?'

'What do you need to find out? How could you find it out?'

'Have you done anything like this before?'

'Does this remind you of anything?'

## Changing a closed question to an open question

Sometimes it is easy to think of a closed question, but not so easy to think of an open one. However, most closed questions can be changed into open questions. Here are some examples:

| Closed questions | Open questions |
| --- | --- |
| Does that symbol mean add or subtract? | What does that symbol mean? |
| Does that fact help you? | How does that fact help you? |
| Can you count the buttons? | How could you count the buttons? |
| What do 4 and 2 and 7 add up to? | What numbers can you make using 4, 2 and 7? |
| What is $6 \times 5$? | If $6 \times 5$ is 30, what else can you work out from that fact? |
| Is 24 an even number? | What even numbers are greater than 10? |

**Language and Mathematics**

## Mathematical vocabulary

Children should gradually build up a knowledge of mathematical words and their meanings. They should be able to understand these words when others use them, and they should be able to use a good vocabulary themselves. The teacher should include specific mathematical words in the lesson plans. The feedback sheet on page 95, for you and the teacher to use, includes a space for special vocabulary: 'Words to use'. The glossary at the back of the book explains some mathematical words.

Pay attention to children's use of mathematical language. When you are aware that children are not using a useful mathematical word, find the right way to drop it into the conversation. You can do this by repeating what they say, but adding the new word. For example:

'You're telling us you've made that plasticine into a square shape, with squares all the way round. So you've made a *cube*. Can anyone else make a cube?'

Sometimes everyday words have a special mathematical meaning. We say, "Just half a cup for me," but we mean, 'not as full as usual' rather than exactly half. In mathematics we expect 'half' to mean precisely half. The word 'difference' also has a special meaning in mathematics. 'The difference between 3 and 5' means comparing the numbers 3 and 5 and looking for a numerical difference. The difference between 3 and 5 is 2 (because 5 is 2 more than 3). We need to explain to children that some words have a special meaning in mathematics. We can then expect children to use words correctly and accurately.

"give children enough time to think of the answer"

## Useful tips

 You can learn a lot about what children do and don't understand by listening to them talk.

 Ask children to explain things to each other, and listen to them. They can learn from each other and you can find out what they know and understand.

 Keep a notebook with you when you work with children. Make a note of things children say that show what they do understand and what they don't understand. Pass this information on to the teacher.

 When you ask children questions, give them time to reply. Try counting to five in your head before you ask another question. Children need enough time to think.

 Encourage children to answer questions with a whole sentence.

 Ask the teacher if there is any special vocabulary you should emphasise over the next two or three weeks.

 Expect children to use the correct mathematical words. Introduce the correct words if the children don't use them.

 Try not to tell children the answers. Ask them questions instead.

# When English is an additional language

Children who are learning English understand all sorts of things about mathematics. However, it isn't easy to find out what they know if they can't tell you. It is useful to know some simple number games and activities that children can play without having to say much. The rules or instructions should be very easy to follow. It's best if children can follow the rules by watching each other, then you don't have to explain. Children who are learning English can play or work with children who understand what to do. You can then watch the children who are learning, to see what they know about numbers.

When children are learning English, you want them to increase their vocabulary and you want to get them to talk. It is important to encourage children to talk in complete sentences — don't let them limit themselves to one- or two-word answers. Turn-taking games are a useful way of learning English and mathematics together. Make sure the game is easy to play, and that children have to say something simple, such as the next number on the card. The child can watch what other players say and do, and join in when they understand what to do.

Sometimes children who are new to the school, and have been taught in a different way, take a while to get used to a new way of learning mathematics. It will take longer if they are also learning to speak English. Some children will be familiar with another number script, and will be learning a new set of symbols. You need to bear all this in mind when working with these children, and give them time and opportunity to show you what they do know.

This game, using number cards, is an example of an activity that requires the children to say numbers out loud.

## Tricksy

**activity for 3 or more children**

**You will need** Number cards 0 to 100 (the pack need not be complete)

**The Activity**

- Shuffle the cards and deal six to each player. Players may look at their cards.

- The first person chooses one of their cards, puts it in the middle of the table, *and says the number*.

- The other players in turn choose a card and put it on the table too, *and say the number*.

- Whoever puts down the highest number wins the trick. (The trick is the set of cards played in that round.)

- Go on until all the cards are played.

**Easier**
Use cards 0 to 20 or 0 to 50.

**Harder**
Look at your cards and decide how many tricks you think you will win.

Write down your guess and see if you can make it come true.

### Questions to ask

What is that number called?

Which of those two numbers is greater?

Can you show me that number on a number line?

**Language and Mathematics**

## 100-grids

100-grids are endlessly useful. You can use them for all kinds of games and activities. There are many different kinds of 100-grid: some simply go from 1 to 100, others show multiplication tables. These will help children learn about numbers in lots of ways. You can get 100 grids in different scripts (Bengali, Chinese, Arabic, and so on). Children are very interested in these, and you can compare the way the numbers look on the grid. You can find the number 44 on each grid and see if it's in the same place and make sure it really is 44. Children who know a particular script can teach the other children about it.

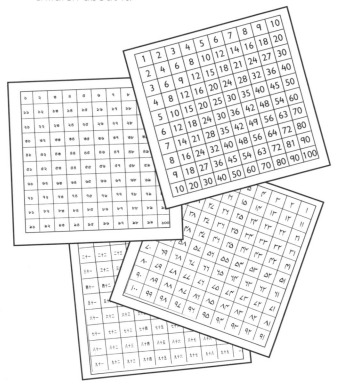

Cut a 100-grid into three or four pieces so that the children can put them back together again by sequencing the numbers correctly. Older children may cope with more pieces.

# Mental Mathematics

" Mathematics is a mental activity — it takes place in the head. "

What are three 9s?

I know three 10s are 30

9 is one less than 10

...so three 9s will be 3 less than 30

It's 27!

Mathematics is a mental activity — it takes place in the head. That's why it can seem difficult. Often, when there is too much to keep in your head at once, you will write things down to keep track of what you are thinking. For example, the greengrocer at the market lists the prices of what he's selling you on a paper bag, then adds it all up at the end. Sometimes he can do the calculation in his head — and if you want to check his arithmetic you have to work it out in your head at the same time. Then you both have to work out the correct change.

Writing numbers down can help you with your calculations because you don't have to remember so much, but the actual mathematics takes place in your mind.

12 13 14 15 16 17

23

Children need to learn lots of mental methods of calculating. Using the right methods makes working things out much quicker and easier. We should talk to children about different methods. We should compare ways of working with numbers to see which ways are easiest and most appropriate. Here are some examples of what children should learn in mental arithmetic:

- remembering number facts like 3 + 7, or 3 × 5, or 24 ÷ 6

- recalling these number facts instantly

- ways of working things out in their heads, given a bit of thinking time, such as 72 − 35, 24 × 3, or 10% of £345

- solving problems like 'Can I buy three 26p stamps for £1?'

> 72 − 35

People have different ways of working out a calculation like 72 − 35. Some methods work very well. Some methods are quicker than others. Children need to talk about and compare different methods. They can learn quicker methods from you and from each other. For example, it is possible to take away 35 one at a time from 72, using your fingers. This could work, but it is slow and unreliable. Here are some other methods that work better, with number line pictures to help describe them:

- take 2 from 72 to make 70, take 30 from 70 to leave 40, take 5 from 40 to make 35, then add the 2 that I took off the 72, to make 37

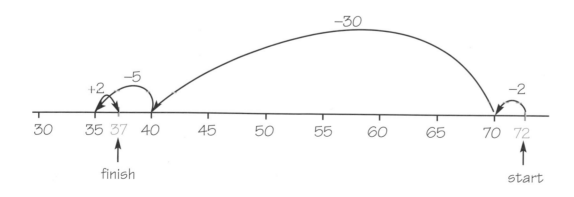

● take 2 from 72 to make 70. I know that double 35 is 70, so I can take away 35, and then I just add 2 to 35 to make 37

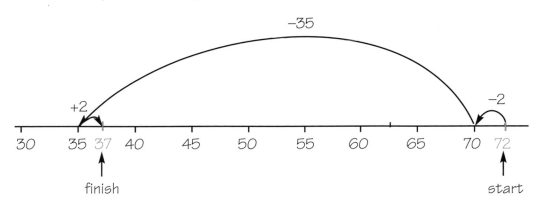

● count on 5 from 35 to 40, count on 32 from 40 to 72, add the 5 and the 32 to make 37

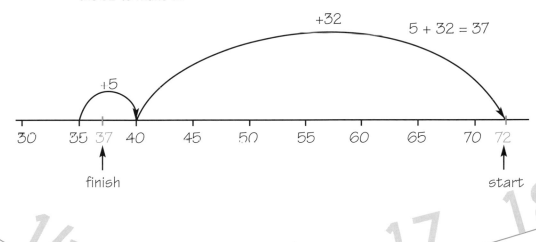

All these methods are good for working out 72 – 35. But to use them you need to know some important things:

● it helps if you know number bonds to 10 — then it's easy adding and taking away in tens

● knowing your number bonds to 10 also makes it easy to take numbers away from a tens number

● it helps if you know doubles of numbers

● it helps if you break up a calculation into smaller parts

● you can use addition to solve a subtraction problem

These are examples of the important things children need to learn about numbers and how they work. Teachers will plan for children to learn particular methods. Talking with children will help them to think about these methods and to learn from you and from each other.

# Writing things down

Children will learn written methods from an early age — but only as a way of keeping track of things that are too long or complicated to do in their heads. Written methods are only helpful when they make mental work easier to do. The important thing is to get children good at working with numbers mentally. What children write down helps us find out how they are working things out. Maths work doesn't have to look neat and tidy to be successful. Encourage children to find helpful ways of using paper and pencil to support the mental work they are doing. Such informal written work is a helpful record of how children are getting on.

While children are learning mental methods, they can jot numbers down as they work to help them remember, like taking notes. They can also practise written calculations, like this, by working them out in their heads:

$$35 + 10 = \square$$

$$17 - \square = 8$$

$$\square + 9 = 28$$

The teacher may ask the children to write down an explanation of how they worked it out.

Encourage children to write a calculation down horizontally, on the same line.

This is so that they can work it out in their own way. If you write a calculation vertically, down the page, like this…

…children will think there is a 'proper' way of doing it. They may then use a long written method, instead of doing it their heads.

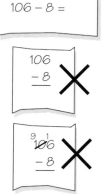

You can take 8 from 106 easily in your head. It's much harder, and quite silly, to use a formal written method that could so easily go wrong, and that children find so difficult.

Older primary children will write down difficult calculations that they can't work out in their heads. They will need to record these neatly in a way that will help them to work them out:

$$
\begin{array}{r}
346 \\
988 \\
+ 465 \\
\hline
\end{array}
$$

$$14\,\overline{|\,1768}$$

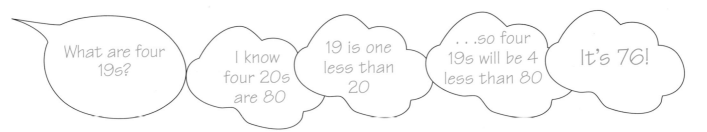

What are four 19s?

I know four 20s are 80

19 is one less than 20

. . .so four 19s will be 4 less than 80

It's 76!

## Useful tips

▶ Mathematics is something we do mentally. Encourage children to work things out in their heads.

▶ Help children learn their number facts and times tables.

▶ Get children to discuss their mental methods with each other and with you. Ask them which methods are the quickest and easiest.

▶ When they are doing sums in their heads children don't need to write anything down unless they are practising, or they are jotting things down to keep track of the calculation.

▶ Encourage children to work things out in their heads, and only use fingers, number lines, or counters when necessary.

▶ There is no 'right' way of working something out in your head. If the method works sensibly, then it's OK.

▶ Give children practical problems to calculate, such as: "Dinner time is at 12.15, and we've got 20 minutes to go. What time is it now?"; "Only three children are allowed in the home corner and there are five in there. How many have to come out?"

▶ When calculations get too hard to do in your head, even if you use jottings to help you, they need to be written down neatly in the conventional way.

## Things to say to the children

● You have both got different answers to that calculation.
Why don't you check your answers?

● How could you check that answer?

● How did you work that out?
Ask this question even when children have got the answer right. Children will know if you only ask this when they get it wrong. And you do want to know how children worked out their calculations.

● Did anyone do it a different way?

● Can you think of a story to go with those numbers?
For example, a story to go with $3 \times 4 = 12$ might be: "three chickens laid four eggs each — how many eggs were there altogether?"

**Mental Mathematics**

2 3 4 5 6 7 8 9 10 11 12 13 14 15 16 17 18 19

# Addition and subtraction

## Start with the bigger number

When adding, start with the bigger number first.

'You need to add 6 and 18? Start with 18 and add on 6.'

> 3 + 8?
> It's better to start with 8 and add on 3.

## Use doubling

When adding a number to itself (doubling) children can often work out the answer easily — for example, 5 + 5 or 60 + 60.

You can use doubling when you want to add two numbers that are nearly doubles — just add or subtract the difference.

> 6 + 6 is 12, so what is 5 + 6 ?

> Two 25s are 50, so what is 27 + 25?

## To add 9, first add 10 then take off 1

If children can add 10 to a number, then they can add 9 — by adding 10 and subtracting 1.

Similarly, if children can subtract 10 from a number, then they can subtract 9 — by taking off 10 and adding back 1.

You can add and subtract 11 easily, too.

> 46 + 9? . . .
> Try 46 + 10 then take away 1.

> What is 27 − 9? . . .
> The same as 27 − 10, then add the 1 back on.

## Do a bit at a time

"You want to subtract 32 from 59?
First do the tens, which is 20.
Now do the ones, that's 7 . . . 20 and 7, that's 27."

"You want to add 17 and 6?
17 is made up of 10 and 7, but let's forget the 10 for a moment.

What is 7 + 6? . . . Yes, double 6 add 1, 13.

Now add on the 10 that we forgot.

What is 13 + 10? . . . Yes, 23."

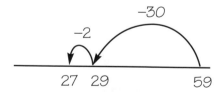

"28  32  36  40  44  48"

# Fill the grid

## You will need

- set of number cards 0–10
- set of number cards 0–20
- a blank 3 × 3 grid
- coloured pens and pencils

**an activity about adding and subtracting mentally**
for 2 or 4 children

1 2 3 4 5 6 7 8 9 10 11 12 13 14 15 16 17 18

## The activity

- Let each child choose a different coloured pen.

- Shuffle each set of cards, and place them face down on the table in their two separate piles.

- Children take turns to:

  – pick a card from each pile

  – add or subtract the two numbers

  – write the answer in any space on the grid

  – return the cards to the bottom of either pile

They carry on until the grid is filled with numbers. You may need to discuss with the children whether they can write the same number in more than one square.

- Next, children take turns to:

  – pick a card from each pile

  – add or subtract the two numbers

  – if the answer is on the grid, they cross it out with their pen

- The winner is the person with the most squares crossed out.

## The aims

- Practising number bonds (see Glossary, p87)
- Working out calculations for numbers up to 30

## Adapting the activity for different ages

### Younger children
Use a 2 × 2 grid and two dice numbered up to 3 or 6

### Older children
Allow subtraction only, or multiplication using cards 2–9
Use cards with numbers up to 100 or 1000

## Questions to ask

→ Which of those two numbers will you start with?

→ Which will give you a bigger answer — adding or subtracting? Try it and see.

→ The last digit here is 4. How could we get 4 by adding two numbers? How could we get 4 by subtracting two numbers?

## Things to notice

### Do children:
→ know their number bonds to 10 (that is, can they add and subtract using any pair of numbers up to 10, such as 4 + 5, 3 + 6 or 9 – 5)?

→ start with the larger number when adding or subtracting?

### Are children:
→ beginning to use some strategies to do mental calculations?

→ able to explain how they did a calculation?

**Mental Mathematics**

# Multiplication and division

## Think about what the answer should look like

When multiplying, children can check their answer by using what they know of the tables.

"All answers in the 2x, 4x, 6x and 8x table are even."

"All answers in the 5x table end in 5 or 0."

"All answers in the 10x table end in 0."

*All answers in the 2x table are even.*

## They can use other checks too

"Halving an odd number gives you a remainder; halving an even number doesn't."

*An even number halved has no remainder.*

## Work it out from a fact you know

"You need to work out 3 × 6 (six threes). You know that 3 × 5 (five threes) are 15. Add one more 3, and the answer is 18."

*Easy. . . five 3s are 15 and one more 3 gives 18.*

## Use doubling

Multiplying by 4 or 8 isn't so hard if children know how to double.

"You need to know 23 × 4? Double 23, then double again."

"To do 8 × 8, start with 8 and double it, then double again, and again."

*23 × 4?*
*Double 23, that's 46 and double again. . . 92.*

## Use halving

Dividing by 4 or 8 isn't so hard if children know how to halve.

"You need to know 124 ÷ 4? You can halve 124, then halve again."

"To do 64 ÷ 8, start with 64 and halve it, then halve again… and again."

*124 ÷ 4?*
*Halve 124, that's 62 and halve again. . . 31.*

" 24    12    6 "

# How many sticks?

**You will need**

- 1–6 dice
- headless matches
- Set of sixteen shape cards (make four of each type)

*Draw the shapes as if they were made from sticks. All the sides should be the same length.*

1 2 3 4 5 6 7 8 9 10 11 12 13 14 15 16 17 18 19

## The activity

- Place the shape cards face down on the table.

  Children take turns to:

  – pick a card

  – throw the dice

The dice shows how many of the shapes the children are to make. The children work out the number of sticks they need. They count out that many sticks, then check by making all the shapes on the table.

How many sticks will be needed to make five triangles?

### The aims

- Building up children's speed, knowledge and confidence
- Practising multiplication number facts

### Adapting the activity for different ages

**Younger children**

Use only triangles (three sides) and pentagons (five sides).

**Older children**

Children don't make the shapes with sticks, but just say the number. It is up to the other players to check whether they got the number right. (They could use a calculator to check.)

or

Instead of dice, use number cards 1–10

or

Use number cards 1–36, which signify a number of sticks, and the shape cards. Children take a shape card and a number card. They read the number, imagine they have that number of sticks and say how many of that shape they could make, and how many sticks (if any) would be left over.

## Questions to ask

→ How can you work that out quickly?

→ Shall we all count in fives together to help?

→ Can you count out the sticks you need in twos?

→ If I give you twelve sticks, how many triangles could you make?

## Things to notice

**Can the children:**

→ count in threes, fours, fives and sixes?

→ explain how they know they've made a mistake? For example: realise that "6 times 3 can't be 17 because all the answers in the 6 times table are even", or "When I multiply by 5, I know the answer must end with a 0 or a 5."

→ use facts they already know to help them work out new ones? For example: "I know 5 times 3 is 15, so 6 times 3 must be 15 add 3."

**Mental Mathematics**

1 2 3 4 5 6 7 8 9 10

# Measures

In this section we look at the following measures, all of which children need to learn about in the primary school:

| length |
|---|

| weight |
|---|

| **volume and capacity** |
|---|

| **time** |
|---|

| money |
|---|

There is a practical activity for each of these measures. All the measures, except time, use metric measurements.

We get better at measuring the more we do it. As adults, most of us have a clear idea of what a pint is and how long a yard is. As we get used to the metric system, we are beginning to be able to judge a kilogram and a metre, too. We know how to do rough measurements without using measuring tools. We can tell by lifting it whether the kettle has enough water in it. We can shake the right amount of coffee into the cup to make it the right strength. We know how big a space we need to park the car. We can tell whether we need one or two shopping bags for all the goods piled up at the supermarket checkout.

Children need lots of practice before they have enough experience to get a feel for what different measurements. Young children misjudge how much water to put in a jug. They are certain they need a huge piece of paper to cut out a small shape. They pick a small piece of paper to wrap a big box.

It takes time for children to build up the practical experience they need to understand measuring. At school we need to give them plenty of opportunities to measure things properly with measuring tools, so that they get used to different metric and imperial measures. We also need to give younger children practical tasks such as mixing paint and cutting paper so that they get a feel for measuring things informally.

*"1 metre"*　　*"36 inches"*
*"24 centimetres"*　*"1 foot"*

# Length

## Basics

There are 100 centimetres in a metre

A metre is a little over a yard — about the distance from an adult's chin to the tip of the index finger, with the arm fully extended

A kilometre is 1000 metres; a distance of 8 kilometres is roughly 5 miles

## Vocabulary to use

long, short, tall, high, low, wide, narrow, deep, shallow, thick, thin, far, near, close, longer/shorter, longest/shortest , metre, centimetre, approximately, estimate, about, roughly

## Useful tips

➤ Make sure children measure from the 0 on tape measures and rulers, and don't count the extra bit before the 0 mark.

➤ If the tape/ruler has centimetres on one side and inches on the other, make sure children know which is which, and use the correct side.

➤ Talk about how much the 'little bits' between the numbers are worth.

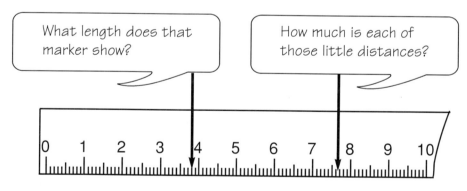

What length does that marker show?

How much is each of those little distances?

➤ Encourage children to record their findings. They could make a simple table.

➤ An estimate is a considered guess. Let children compare their estimates with their measured results — this will help them to estimate more accurately in the future.

This is one way of recording the activity opposite.

|  | nearest wall | furthest wall | comments |
|---|---|---|---|
| estimate | 5 m | 17 m |  |
| measured | 3½ m | 25 m |  |
|  |  |  |  |

# What's the distance?

## You will need

- chalk
- metre sticks

1 2 3 4 5 6 7 8 9 10 11 12 13 14 15 16 17 18

## The activity

Say to the children…

- Stand anywhere in the hall (or playground) and mark where your feet are.

- Estimate the distance from where you are standing to the nearest wall. Write down your estimate.

- Now measure the actual distance, using a metre rule, and write that down.

- Estimate the distance from where you are standing to the furthest wall. Write down your estimate.

- Now measure the actual distance, using a metre rule, and write that down.

- Stand about 3 metres from one of the walls.

- Find out how good your estimate of 3 metres is by measuring the actual distance.

### The mathematics they will practise

- making sensible estimates
- using a metre rule
- recording estimates and measurements
- measuring length with some accuracy
- getting a feel for how long a metre is

### Adapting the activity for different ages

**Younger children**
Children count strides (large steps) instead of using metre sticks

**Older children (Years 5 and 6)**
Children use a surveyor's tape instead of metre sticks to measure longer distances. Most surveyor's tapes are measured in tenths of a metre.

## Questions to ask

→ What does 'estimate' mean? Will a wild guess do?

→ Can you see an imaginary metre rule in your head? Can you imagine measuring from here to the wall with it? Does that help you estimate?

→ Now you have measured about half of the distance, would you like to change your estimate?

→ You say the distance is four metres and a bit. Can you be more accurate about how much the 'bit' is? About half a metre? A quarter of a metre? How many centimetres are there in a metre?

## Things to notice

**Can the children:**
→ use what they know about metres to help them estimate?

→ measure from zero when using a metre rule, or do they simply measure from the beginning of the stick?

→ mark carefully on the floor where the end of the metre stick comes each time, or do they work haphazardly?

→ suggest ways of measuring the 'bit' when the distance is not exactly whole metres? For example, say, "It's half a metre," or "It's about 10 cm"

→ know how to use a metre stick to measure centimetres, or do they count from the wrong end?

→ make more accurate estimates with practice?

*"1 kilogram"*   *"16 ounces"*
*"20 grammes"*   *"1 pound"*

# Weight

## Basics

The units of weight used in schools are grams (shortened to g) and kilograms (shortened to kg)

There are 1000 grams in a kilogram

There are about 30 grams in an ounce, and a kilogram is just over two pounds

Stones, pounds and ounces, known as imperial measures, are being phased out — but children do need to know something about these units too

## Vocabulary to use

heavy, light, heavier, lighter, heaviest, lightest

weighs, balances

gram (g), kilogram (kg)

estimate, roughly, nearly, approximately, about the same as, in between

## Useful tips

➤ If using kitchen-type scales with a dial, make sure the pointer is set at 0 when the pan is empty.

➤ Check that children know what units they are using — grams, kilograms, ounces, and so on.

➤ Talk about how much the 'little bits' between the numbers are worth.

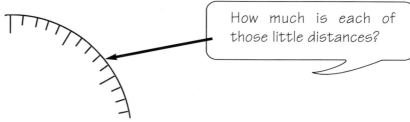

> How much is each of those little distances?

➤ Encourage the children to record their findings. They could make a simple table.

➤ An estimate is a considered guess. Let children compare their estimates with their weighed results — this will help them to estimate more accurately in the future.

This is one way of recording the activity opposite.

> This is the order we think they are in. We think the water is heaviest and the flour is lightest.

|  | heaviest |  |  |  | lightest |
|---|---|---|---|---|---|
| estimated | water | sand | soil | rice | flour |
| weighed |  |  |  |  |  |

# Find the heaviest

## You will need

- five pots, all the same size (for example, yoghurt pots)
- materials to fill the pots (water, sand, rice, pebbles…)
- weighing balance (for younger children)
- weighing scales (for older children)
- a selection of weights  (10 g, 100 g, 500 g…)

**an activity about weighing for 2 or 3 children**

1 2 3 4 5 6 7 8 9 10 11 12 13 14 15 16 17

## The activity

Ask the children to…

- Take a pot each and fill it — they should each choose a different material with which to fill their pot.

- Work as a group to put the pots in order, heaviest first — estimating only at this stage. In order to do this, children will need to compare two pots at a time, by holding one in each hand, then another two, and so on.

- When they have finished, ask them to record their estimates in some way.

- They should then use the balance or the scales to weigh the pots.

## The mathematics they will practise

- making sensible estimates
- using simple weighing instruments
- recording estimates and measurements
- weighing with some accuracy
- reading scales with some accuracy
- learning the number of grams in a kilogram (1000 grams)

## Adapting the activity for different ages

**Younger children**
Stick to just three pots

**Older children**
Children could use the balance and weights to find out the weight of each pot in grams, then put them in order.
Children could use the scales to find out the weight of each pot in grams, then put them in order.

## Questions to ask

→ What do people use to weigh things?

→ Do you think all the pots weigh the same? Why do you think that?

→ What is meant by 'estimating'? Does it just mean guessing? An estimate is a *considered* guess — for instance, a guess made after picking the pots up and noticing how heavy they feel.

→ Which do you think is the heaviest of all the pots? And which do you think is the lightest? Why do you think that?

→ How good was your estimating? Do you think you would be more accurate another time?

## Things to notice

**Can the children:**
→ use a balance and weights to weigh an object?

→ read the dial on the scales? Do they understand the intervals between the numbers?

**Measures**

*"24 cubic centimetres"*

*"2 pints"*

*"50 millilitres"*

*"55 litres"*

# Volume and capacity

## Basics

Liquid volumes are measured in litres (shortened to l) and millilitres (shortened to ml)

Solid volumes are measured in cubic centimetres (shortened to cc)
— a Centicube, for example, has a volume of 1 cc (or 1 cm³)

There are 1000 millilitres in a litre

A litre is just over two pints

Pints and gallons, known as imperial measures, are being phased out — but children do need to know something about these units too

## Vocabulary to use

full, empty, holds, brim, overflowing
holds most, holds least, amount, refill
litre, half litre, millilitre
funnel, container, cylinder
estimate, roughly, approximately, nearly, about the same as

## Useful tips

➤ Keep children's work away from water.
Don't use sand and water in the same lesson!

➤ Check that children know what units they are using
— millilitres, litres, pints, fluid ounces, and so on.

➤ Help children practise how to read
calibrations on jugs and cylinders.

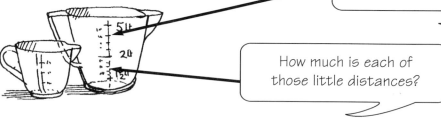

How much water does that mark represent?

How much is each of those little distances?

➤ Encourage the children to record their findings. They could make a simple table.

➤ An estimate is a considered guess. Let children compare their estimates with their measured results — this will help them to estimate more accurately in the future.

This is one way of recording the activity opposite.

|  | | estimate | measured | comments |
|---|---|---|---|---|
| more than 1 litre | | shampoo bottle | yes | |
| about 1 litre | | yoghurt pot | no | |
|  | | | | |

# Hunt the container

**an activity about measuring volume**
for 2 or 4 children

## You will need

- materials that can be poured (water, sand, rice…)
- slips of paper marked:

| | |
|---|---|
| more than 1 litre | about 2 litres |
| more than ½ litre but less than 1 litre | |
| less than ½ litre | about 1½ litres |
| more than 1 litre but less than 2 litres | |
| about 500 millilitres | |

- a selection of plastic bottles, jars and bowls that match the capacities marked on the cards. You may want to label them A, B, C and so on.
- measuring jugs and cylinders 500 ml, 1000 ml…

1 2 3 4 5 6 7 8 9 10 11 12 13 14 15 16 17 18

## The activity

- Deal out the slips of paper so that each child has one or more. Each child or pair of children has to select a container which they estimate will hold roughly the amount written on their card.

- Children fill their containers with sand or water. They pour the contents into a measuring jug and measure the quantity. They record their results.

## The mathematics they will practise

- making sensible estimates
- using calibrated containers for measuring capacity
- reading capacity scales
- recording estimates and measurements

## Adapting the activity for different ages

### Younger children
Stick to finding containers that are either 'more than 1 litre' or 'less than 1 litre'

### Older children
Use slips of paper with more difficult specifications such as:

| | | |
|---|---|---|
| ½ litre to 750 ml | 10 ml to ¼ litre | 50 ml to 100 ml |
| less than 5 ml | between 250 ml and 500 ml | |

## Questions to ask

→ Do you think that jug can hold more than one litre? Or less?

→ What can you use to help you make a good estimate? Encourage the children to look at a measuring jug to find out how much a litre is.

→ Which is the most sensible measuring jug to use for finding the capacity of that jar?

→ Is that more or less than one litre? How do you know?

→ Are you surprised by any of the results?

## Things to notice

**Can the children:**

→ tell that a tall, thin container holds less than a short, squat one?

→ compare the capacity of two containers by pouring from one to the other? Do they take notice of overflowing? Do they notice space left at the top?

→ make sensible estimates when choosing jugs to use for measuring?

→ work carefully and accurately?

→ read the calibrations in the measuring jug?

**Measures**

"5 minutes"    "30 minutes"
        "10 seconds"
                    "24 hours"

# Time

## Basics

There are 60 seconds in one minute

There are 60 minutes in one hour

There are 24 hours in one day

An 'analogue' clock is one with rotating hands

A 'digital' clock displays the time in digits

## Vocabulary to use

clock, watch, o'clock, face, digital, analogue, minute hand, hour hand
early, late, earlier, later, earliest, latest, fast, slow
midnight, midday, noon, hour, minute, second

## Useful tips

➤ Practise reading the time with children whenever the opportunity occurs — using both school clocks and wrist watches.

➤ Talk about the time of day when things happen: "Lunch is at half past twelve. Can you show me where the hands will be at half past twelve?"

➤ Talk about time passing. "There are five minutes left before playtime. It's time to pack up."

# Find the pairs

## You will need

- 15 cards showing random times in digital form (stick to multiples of 5 minutes)

- 15 cards showing the same times in analogue (clockface) form. These cards could be made using a clock stamp

- a real digital timepiece (for example a child's watch), and a real analogue timepiece (for example a school clock) would also be useful

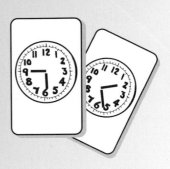

1 2 3 4 5 6 7 8 9 10 11 12 13 14 15 16 17 18 19

## The activity

◆ Put the digital cards face down in a pile on the table. Spread the analogue cards out on the table face up.

◆ Each child takes a card in turn from the pile of digital cards, and says the time shown. Then the child finds the matching analogue card from the table. The children hold onto their pairs: the player with the most cards at the end of the game is the winner.

◆ If a child makes a mistake, the digital card goes back to the bottom of the pile and the analogue card remains face up on the table.

◆ When the children have finished they can play again, this time putting the analogue cards in a pile and spreading the digital cards face up.

## The mathematics they will practise

◆ counting in fives
◆ reading the time in five-minute intervals on digital clocks
◆ telling the time in five-minute intervals on analogue clocks
◆ recognising equivalent forms of the same time

## Adapting the activity for different ages

**Younger children**
Stick to simple times: o'clock, half past, quarter to, quarter past.

**Older children**
Use cards showing 'harder' times, such as 7:21pm.
Use cards showing times on the 24-hour clock, such as 19:21.

## Questions to ask

➜ Look at this watch. Which hand shows the minutes? Which hand shows the hours?

➜ Look at this digital watch. Which number shows the minutes? And which number shows the hours?

➜ How many minutes after 2 o'clock is quarter past 2? You can use a real clock to help you work it out.

➜ What time does this card show? What do you normally do at this time of day?

## Things to notice

**Can the children:**
➜ work out the analogue time by counting in fives using a clockface?

➜ work out digital time — especially between half past the hour and the hour, for example, 7:35?

➜ understand that 'five past' is written with a zero, for example, 9:05?

41

**Measures**

# Money

## Basics

100 pence is £1

## Vocabulary to use

penny, pound
how many, how many more, how many fewer

## Useful tips

▶ Allow children to handle real coins whenever possible — for example, when shopping or handling dinner money.

▶ Use real coins when playing games. Counting how many there are at the start, and checking at the end, is a valuable mathematics activity in itself.

▶ Some children are good at calculating with money. Use this to help them with other mental maths: "You need to add 23 and 36. Imagine that's 23p and 36p; can you add up those amounts?"

# Make it up to ...

### You will need

- a saucer of 1p coins
- money dice showing '1p, 1p, 2p, 2p, 3p, 3p'

**an activity about adding coins
for 3 or 5 children**

## The activity

Say to the children...

- Agree who will start. That person tosses the dice.

- What does the dice say? Can you read out the number of pennies it says?

- Now take that number of pennies from the saucer.

- How many more pennies do you need to make it up to five? Take that number of pennies too.

- Now check whether you were right.

- Now it's the next person's turn.

## Questions to ask

→ How did you work that out?

→ Can you show me on your fingers how many more pennies you will need?

→ Do you need to count those pennies again? Cover them up with your hand and tell me how many you have.

## Things to notice

**Can the children:**

→ 'just say' how many more pennies they need to make five?

→ 'just say' how many more pennies they need to make ten?

→ use their fingers to work out how many more pennies they need to make five?

→ use their fingers to work out how many more pennies they need to make ten?

### The mathematics they will practise

- familiarity with coins
- adding numbers mentally to make five

### Adapting the activity for different ages

**Younger children**
Use a dice with dots 1, 2, 3. Children use a board marked with 10 or 12 pennies. They collect pennies and fill up the board

**Older children**
Use 2p as well as 1p pieces

Play 'Make it up to 10', using the same dice. Children say how many pence they need to make the number up to ten

Use a dice showing '1p, 2p, 3p, 4p, 5p, 6p' and play 'Make it up to 20'

# Activities

# Mathematical Games and Activities

Games help children with learning. Because games are fun, children want to play them. Games get children to talk to each other about what they are learning. Games let children feel in charge.

## Games for small groups

There are games in this section for each age group. The games are simple and can be adapted for younger and older children. Talk to the teacher about the learning objectives for each game.

The games are supported by:

◆ questions to ask children to make them think about the mathematics

◆ things to notice about what children are learning. You can make a note of these and tell the teacher about progress children make, and problems they might have.

◆ ways to adapt the activity for younger and older children

◆ information on the mathematics the children will practise

## Activities for large groups

There is also a selection of shorter activities you can use when you are working with a larger group. Each activity in this section lasts only five minutes or so, but you can extend them or string several together to keep children busy for longer periods of time.

## Useful tips

➤ Build up a collection of activities to play with children at odd moments, such as 'I spy numbers', or playing number games with car registration numbers.

➤ Collect together the things you need for each game. Put them in a zipped plastic wallet with a list of contents. Children can check that nothing is missing at the end of the game.

➤ Teach one group how to play a game. Ask a reliable child to teach the game to another group. Children can learn the game from each other.

➤ Children can suggest ideas for changing the games to make them harder or easier, or more interesting. Make a note of their ideas.

➤ Discuss with the children the mathematics they have been practising. This helps children to apply their newly learned skills in other mathematical contexts.

# Give-away

## You will need

- an ordinary dice
- three or four saucers or tubs, each containing ten counters (or buttons, or shells)

**an activity about counting to 10 for 3 or 4 children**

1 2 3 4 5 6 7 8 9 10 11 12 13 14 15 16 17

## The activity

- Children take turns to toss the dice, say the number, and give that number of counters to the child on their right.
  If they don't have enough counters to do this, they have to miss a go.
- The person on the left takes the next turn.
- The winner is the first one to get rid of all their counters.

## The mathematics they will practise

- counting to 10
- recognising the numbers on a dice

## Changing the activity for different ages

**Younger children**

Use a dice marked '1, 1, 2, 2, 3, 3' and five counters

**Older children**

Use two dice and add the numbers together; you will need 20 counters each

## Questions to ask

➜ What number did you get?

➜ How many counters must you give to Sasha?

➜ How many counters have you got now? Can you count them?

➜ If Joe gives you five counters, how many will you have? And how many will Joe have left?

## Things to notice

**Can the children:**

➜ recognise the pattern of dots on the dice without having to count?

➜ give the correct number of counters?

➜ check that they are being given the correct number of counters?

➜ count accurately?

➜ count how many counters they have after each go?

➜ tell their left from their right?

➜ say their number bonds — or are they using their fingers to help them?

**Games for small groups**

# More than/less than

### You will need

- counters
- dice made from a wooden or plastic cube, with three sides marked 'more than' and three sides marked 'less than', or a 'more than/less than' spinner
- number cards 0–10

## The activity

◆ Put the number cards face down in a pile on the table.

◆ Two of the children take turns to pick the top card, say the number, and take that many counters.

◆ The third child tosses the dice and reads aloud the result — 'more than' or 'less than'.

◆ If it is 'less than', whichever child has fewer counters than their partner must say how many fewer they have. If it is 'more than', whichever child has more counters than their partner must say how many more they have.

◆ The child who gets to say the sentence about 'more' or 'less' gains a point — if they say it correctly.

◆ The first person to score five points becomes the dice-thrower.

### Variation

- Use cards 1–5 or cards 0–20.

1 2 3 4 5 6 7 8 9 10 11 12 13 14 15 16 17 18 19

# Make 20

### You will need

- two sets of number cards 0–10, shuffled

## The activity

◆ Divide the cards between the two children.

The aim is to make as many rows of cards as possible that add up to 20.

They score five points for every row of 20.

| 8 | 3 | 5 | 4 |

### Variation

- Children can make agreed swaps with each other.

# Take it

You will need

- two ordinary dice
- number cards 2–12

## The activity

◆ The children lay out the cards in order, face up.
They take turns to toss the two dice and add the numbers together.
They take that number card (if it hasn't been taken already).

◆ The person who collects the most cards is the winner.

Variation

- Use cards 0–12, and let children add or subtract the two numbers,
  or
- Use 10-sided dice and number cards up to 20.

1 2 3 4 5 6 7 8 9 10 11 12 13

# Number jigsaw

You will need

- number line 0–30 or a 100-grid, cut up into five or six pieces

## The activity

◆ The children jumble the pieces up, then piece them together to
reconstruct the number line or square.

1 2 3 4 5 6 7 8 9 10

# Number books

You will need

- sheets of paper, plain or coloured

## The activity

◆ The children choose three sheets of paper and stack these together.
They staple or sew the pages in the middle, and fold the sheets to
make a little book.

◆ Children choose a number. This number is the theme of their book.
They then fill the pages with information and images relating to that
number. They could:
  - look in magazines for printed versions of the number
  - collect instances of the number appearing in door numbers,
    telephone numbers or bus numbers
  - make up calculations that have that number as the answer

**Games for small groups**

# Snake pit

**You will need**

- pencil and paper
- two dice

*1  2  3  4  5  6  7  8  9  10  11  12  13  14  15  16  17  18  19*

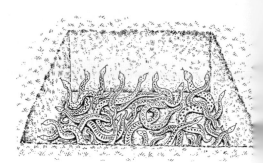

## The activity

Children begin with a score of 0. The aim is to add numbers together to reach 50 without falling in the Snake Pit.

These numbers are in the Snake Pit:

### 10    20    30    40

If a child scores a total of one of these numbers at any point in the game they fall in the Snake Pit and lose a point.

- ◆ The children take it in turns to roll two dice and choose one of the numbers and add it to their current score.

- ◆ If they land in the Snake Pit they lose a point; if they manage to avoid it, they gain a point.

- ◆ They then pass the dice on to the next child.

- ◆ The game ends when anyone reaches 50 or goes past it.

- ◆ Children keep a written record of their score as they go along.

**Questions to ask**

→ Which of the numbers are you going to choose to add? Why are you picking that one?

→ What will you get if you add that number to your current score?

→ Can you say the answer without using your fingers?

→ What number do you need to reach 50?

## Things to notice

**Can the children:**

→ work out what will happen if they choose this or that number, then choose a sensible number to add so as to avoid landing in the Snake Pit?

→ add the numbers mentally?

→ use their fingers to help them add?

### The mathematics they will practise

- ◆ mental addition
- ◆ making numbers up to 10 and tens numbers
- ◆ making choices

### Adapting the activity for different ages

**Younger children**

Use two dice, both marked '1, 1, 2, 2, 3, 3' and aim for 20. The Snake Pit contains the numbers 5, 10, 15 and 20.

**Older children**

Start with 100 and aim to reach 0. Roll three dice and choose two of the numbers to add together, then subtract the result from the total in the display; the Snake Pit contains the numbers 10, 20, 30, 40, 50, 60, 70, 80 and 90.

# Descriptions

## You will need

- number cards 0–50
- about 50 labels with brief descriptions of numbers for example:

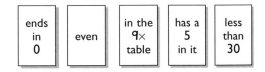

ends in 0 | even | in the 9× table | has a 5 in it | less than 30

## 50 ideas for labels

| | |
|---|---|
| ends in 0 | has a 7 in it |
| ends in 1 | has a 8 in it |
| ends in 2 | has a 9 in it |
| ends in 3 | less than 50 |
| ends in 4 | less than 45 |
| ends in 5 | less than 40 |
| ends in 6 | less than 35 |
| ends in 7 | less than 30 |
| ends in 8 | less than 25 |
| ends in 9 | less than 20 |
| in the 9× table | less than 15 |
| in the 8× table | less than 10 |
| in the 7× table | less than 5 |
| in the 6× table | more than 45 |
| in the 5× table | more than 40 |
| In the 4× table | more than 35 |
| in the 3× table | more than 30 |
| in the 2× table | more than 25 |
| has a 0 in it | more than 20 |
| has a 1 in it | more than 15 |
| has a 2 in it | more than 10 |
| has a 3 in it | more than 5 |
| has a 4 in it | even number |
| has a 5 in it | odd number |
| has a 6 in it | prime number |

## The activity

If there are more than three children, tell them to work in pairs so that they have someone to discuss their choices with.

- Shuffle the labels and give nine to each player. The players arrange their labels in front of them.

- Shuffle the number cards and put them in a pile on the table, face down. This is the pick-up pile.

- The first player takes the top number card and says the number. He decides whether it belongs with any of his labels. If it does, he places it on the label. If it doesn't, he puts the number card face up on a throw-away pile.

- The next player can take either the top card from the throw-away pile or the top card from the pick-up pile. She finds a place for the card on her labels — or discards it if there's nowhere to put it.

- Players continue like this until somebody has covered all nine of their labels. This person is the winner.

### The mathematics they will practise

- thinking about whether a number is greater than or smaller than another number
- learning odd and even numbers
- learning multiplication tables

### Adapting the activity for different ages

**Younger children**

Each child has five easier labels.

**Older children**

Use number cards 0–100.

Get children to make up their own property labels to add to the set.

## Questions to ask

→ Read your labels out one by one. Does that one apply to your number? What about that one?

→ Tell me some numbers that could go on that label. Are there lots of numbers that could go there, or only a few?

→ Could that number card go on more than one label?

→ Which label will you choose to put that card on? Why?

## Things to notice

**Can the children:**

→ read a label and identify some numbers that could go on it?

→ say which numbers are odd and which are even?

→ say whether a number is greater than or smaller than another number?

→ say whether a number is in a particular times table?

# Number squares

You will need

● a set of number cards 0–20 for each child

## The activity

◆ Each child chooses nine of their cards and arranges them in a 3 × 3 square.

◆ They then find the total for each column and row. Ask them to rearrange the cards and find the totals again. How many different answers can they make?

Variation

● Use cards with higher numbers.

an activity about adding
for any number of children

```
 1   6   9
 7  15   2
 3  12  18
```

1 2 3 4 5 6 7 8 9 10 11 12 13 14 15 16 17 18 19

# Making numbers

This is a game for two children working together. A larger group can be split up into pairs, each pair working on the activity at their own pace.

an activity about adding and multiplying
for 2 children working together

You will need

● four ordinary dice
● pencil and paper
● a 100-grid
● felt-tipped pens

## The activity

◆ The children toss all four dice, and write down the numbers that come up.

◆ They now use those numbers in any way to make as many different numbers as they can. For example, with 1, 4, 4 and 6, one child could make:

$14 + 46 = 60$   $6 + 1 + 4 + 4 = 15$   $6 + 1 = 7$

$4 + 4 = 8$   $7 \times 8 = 56$   and so on…

◆ They record their calculations on paper.

◆ They cross off the numbers they make on a 100-grid. How many different numbers can they make this way?

Variation

● Use cards with higher numbers.

| 1 | 2 | 3 | 4 | 5 | 6 | 7 | 8 | 9 | 10 |
|---|---|---|---|---|---|---|---|---|---|
| 11 | 12 | 13 | 14 | 15 | 16 | 17 | 18 | 19 | 20 |
| 21 | 22 | 23 | 24 | 25 | 26 | 27 | 28 | 29 | 30 |
| 31 | 32 | 33 | 34 | 35 | 36 | 37 | 38 | 39 | 40 |
| 41 | 42 | 43 | 44 | 45 | 46 | 47 | 48 | 49 | 50 |
| 51 | 52 | 53 | 54 | 55 | 56 | 57 | 58 | 59 | 60 |
| 61 | 62 | 63 | 64 | 65 | 66 | 67 | 68 | 69 | 70 |
| 71 | 72 | 73 | 74 | 75 | 76 | 77 | 78 | 79 | 80 |
| 81 | 82 | 83 | 84 | 85 | 86 | 87 | 88 | 89 | 90 |
| 91 | 92 | 93 | 94 | 95 | 96 | 97 | 98 | 99 | 100 |

# Four in a line

## You will need

- a 100-grid
- four 1–6 dice
- counters
- calculators or a tables chart
- pencil and paper

| 1 | 2 | 3 | 4 | 5 | 6 | 7 | 8 | 9 | 10 |
|---|---|---|---|---|---|---|---|---|---|
| 11 | 12 | 13 | 14 | 15 | 16 | 17 | 18 | 19 | 20 |
| 21 | ● | 23 | 24 | | | | 28 | 29 | 30 |
| 31 | 32 | ● | 34 | 35 | 36 | 37 | 38 | 39 | 40 |
| 41 | 42 | 43 | ● | 45 | 46 | 47 | 48 | 49 | 50 |
| 51 | 52 | 53 | 54 | ● | 56 | 57 | | 59 | 60 |
| 61 | ● | 63 | 64 | 65 | 66 | 67 | 68 | 69 | 70 |
| 71 | 72 | 73 | 74 | 75 | 76 | 77 | 78 | 79 | 80 |
| 81 | 82 | 83 | 84 | 85 | | 87 | 88 | 89 | 90 |
| 91 | 92 | 93 | 94 | 95 | 96 | 97 | 98 | 99 | 100 |

## The activity

This is a game for one child, or two children working together.
A larger group can be split up into pairs, each pair working on the activity together.

- The children toss all four dice, then make sums by adding and multiplying the dice numbers in any way they choose.

  For instance, with 2, 3, 4 and 4 they might do:

  $2 + 3 = 5$    $4 + 4 = 8$    $5 \times 8 = 40$    $2 + 3 + 4 = 9$    $9 \times 4 = 36$

- They then cover the numbers they come up with on the hundred grid.

- The aim is to cover four numbers in a line.

## The mathematics they will practise

- mental addition
- mental multiplication
- recall of multiplication facts

## Adapting the activity for different ages

### Younger children

Use two dice or number cards 1–10.

### Older children

Use dice with bigger numbers:

1–12,  1–10,  1–20

Include subtraction and division.

## Questions to ask

→ What different numbers could you make with those dice numbers? Are there any others you could make? How do you know?

## Things to notice

**Can the children:**
→ recall multiplication facts up to $5 \times 5$ instantly?

→ recall multiplication facts up to $10 \times 10$ instantly?

→ work out multiplications up to $5 \times 5$ mentally?

→ work out multiplications up to $10 \times 10$ mentally?

**Games for small groups**

# Secret number

You will need

- a 100-grid covered in tacky-back (this is useful as the players can cross out numbers they have eliminated)
- felt-tipped pens
- pencil and paper

## The activity

- One child is the Thinker. The Thinker chooses a number in secret and writes it on a scrap of paper, which is hidden away until the end of the game.

- The other players, the Guessers, take turns to ask questions about the number, to which the Thinker can only respond with 'yes' or 'no'.

- The aim of the Guessers is to find out the number by asking as few questions as possible. They can keep track of how many questions they ask, and see if they can find the secret number with fewer questions next time.

### Variation

- use numbers to 1000, or fractions or decimals, or negative numbers

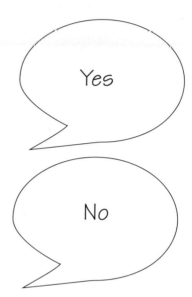

1 2 3 4 5 6 7 8 9 10 11 12 13 14 15 16 17 18 19

# 5-minute Activities for large groups

How many ways can I make . . .?

What does 5 add 4 make?

1 2 3 4 5 6 7 8 9 10 11 12 13

When you work with a large group, choose activities that involve everybody, so that all the children can join in. Make sure the activities are fast-moving — the children will enjoy the pace and it will keep them thinking.

The activities in this section are all very short — but they can easily be extended or strung together for longer sessions.

The activities in this section are for children in Years 1 and above. If you are working with children in the Reception class, try some of the number rhymes suggested on p61.

# Counting activities

**Count forwards in ones to 20 (or 10) and back again**

'What number comes before 6? After 13?'

> What number comes before 6?

**Count round the circle in ones, forwards or backwards**

Children who say a tens number (10, 20, 30 and so on) stand up and drop out of the counting.

'Who is going to stand up next?'

'If we count to 50 how many people will be standing?'

'How many will still be sitting?'

**Count in twos from 2 to 30 and back again**

'What are those numbers called?' [even numbers]

'Tell me some of the numbers we don't count...'

'What are they called?' [odd numbers]

**Count in twos from 1 to 31, and back again**

'Those are the odd numbers, aren't they?'

'Do we ever count a tens number this way?'

'Why not?'

> 1, 3, 5, 7 . . .

**Count in fives to 30**

'If we go on, will we say the number 43?'

'How do you know?'

**Count in tens to 100 and back again to zero**

'Why is it easy to count in tens?'

**Count the children in the group**

'How many eyes/fingers have you all got?'

'How many hands/feet are there in the room? Don't forget your own!'

# A game

**Pairs to 10**

This a good way of practising the number pairs
that make ten:

    10 + 0    9 + 1    8 + 2    7 + 3    and so on.

◆ Choose a number, such as 4, and say:

  "I say 4; you say…".

◆ The group should respond with 6, the number that makes it up to 10.

# On the blackboard

Use the board for writing down children's suggestions.

**Missing number**

◆ Write the numbers 1 to 10 on the board.

◆ Get the children to close their eyes.

◆ Cover one of the numbers up with your hand.

◆ Tell them to open their eyes and then ask:
"What number is hidden?"

**Making 10p**

◆ 'How many different ways can you
make 10p using 1p, 2p and 5p coins?'

How many
different
ways . . .

**Activities for large group**

# Counting activities

**Count in fives from 1 to 51 and back again**

'Tell me some of the numbers we don't use.'

> 51, 46, 41, 36, 31, 26. . .

**Count in fives to 99**

'What would the next number be? How do you know?'

**Count in tens**

'Count in tens to 200 and back again to zero.'

> 10, 20, 30, 40. . .

# Games

**Pairs to 30**

◆ Practise number pairs that make 30: 20 + 10, 19 + 11, and so on.

◆ Choose a number, such as 14, and say:

"I say 14; you say…".

The group should respond with 16, the number that makes it up to 30.

Ask one of the children to check the answer with a calculator.

**Buzz!**

◆ Count round the circle in ones. The child who should say three says "Buzz!" instead. As the game goes on, each child who should say a multiple of three says "Buzz" instead.
So the counting goes:
1, 2, Buzz!, 4, 5, Buzz!, 7, 8, Buzz!, and so on.

◆ After a while change the Buzz! numbers to multiples of five:
1, 2, 3, 4, Buzz!, 6, 7, 8, 9, Buzz!, and so on.

> 1, 2, Buzz!, 4, 5, Buzz! . . .

# On the blackboard

Use the board for writing down children's suggestions.

**Making 12**

◆ Write the numbers 1 to 8 on the board.

'How many ways can you make 12 by adding three of these numbers?'

'How about making 13?'

'How many ways can you make 20?'

**Different sums**

◆ 'How many different sums can you make using the numbers 2 and 5 and the + and − signs?'

$$2 + 5 = \qquad 2 + 5 - 2 =$$

**Answers**

◆ 'Now, as I point to the sums, you all call out the answers.'

**Making 50p**

◆ 'How many different ways can you make 50p using only the silver coins?'

How many different ways. . . ?

59

# Counting activities

**Count in 20s to 1000, and back again to zero**

'How many 20s are there in 100?' (answer: 5)

'How many 20s are there in 500?' (answer: 25)

'How many 20s are there in 580?' (answer: 29)

# On the blackboard

Use the board for writing down children's suggestions.

**Making 100**

◆ 'Add any three numbers between 20 and 50 to make 100. You can't use the same number twice, and you must use exactly three numbers.'

◆ Ask another child to check.

**Different sums**

◆ 'What different calculations can you make using the numbers 2 and 5 and the × sign? You can use each number as often as you like.'

$$2 \times 5 = \qquad 25 \times 2 = \qquad 52 \times 5 =$$

**Answers**

◆ Write some sums on the board.

◆ Point to the sums, and ask everyone to call out the answers.

◆ Ask one of the children to check the answer.

**Guess**

◆ Write a number on the board (say, 9). The children think up calculations that have that number as their answer. Encourage children to challenge each other if they think a calculation is wrong, and get them to check.

? + ? + ? = 100

Nine... er... 3 times 3

Ninety-nine minus ninety

# Stories, Songs and Rhymes

Many stories, songs and rhymes involve mathematics. *Goldilocks and the Three Bears,* for example, involves numbers (chairs, bowls and beds), and sizes (of bears, chairs, bowls and beds). Some songs and rhymes are written specifically to help children learn about counting.

Most of these rhymes are for young children, from the nursery to Year 1 or 2. At this age, children love to hear you repeat stories and rhymes that they know well. You can repeat them in different ways, using number cards and props such as hats to add interest and help with the counting.

> " to hear the same stories and songs many times is a good way to learn "

# Stories

"2    4    6    8    10    12"

Fairy stories and other tales often have mathematics 'hidden' inside them. When you tell these stories, or children act them out or draw them, you can help them focus on the mathematics, by talking about the events and characters.

## Goldilocks and the Three Bears

> Focusing on height and size

◆ 'Draw the three bears, then cut them out..'

◆ 'How can you make sure that Father Bear is taller than the other two?'

◆ 'Draw Goldilocks too. She is the same size as Mother Bear, isn't she? Can you make her the same size in the picture?'

> Putting things in order of size

◆ 'Let's pretend these three teddies are the three bears.'

◆ 'Can you say which bear is which?  Can you put them in order of size?'

◆ 'Which bowl of porridge is the biggest, to give to Father Bear? Which is the smallest, for Baby Bear? Which is the medium-sized one for Mother Bear?'

# Cinderella

Focusing on size

◆ 'Let's play at Cinderella and see if this shoe fits any of you.'

Matching pairs

◆ 'Here is the shoe that the Prince found.
Can you look in this jumble of shoes and find its partner?'

# The Sleeping Beauty

Counting

◆ 'The Sleeping Beauty was asleep for a hundred years.
Can any of you help me count to a hundred?'

## Useful tips

 When you are reading or telling a story, encourage the children to join in:

– ask them to show you with their hands the size of Father Bear's bowl

– get them to help you count the number of people pulling at the enormous turnip

– ask them to tell you what the clock looked like when it struck midnight at Cinderella's ball

63

# Songs and Rhymes

You can use songs and rhymes to teach some mathematics to younger children in a fun and rhythmical way.

## Build a House with Five Bricks

" Build a house with five bricks,

One, two, three, four, five.

Put a roof on top

And a chimney too,

Where the wind blows through:

Whoo-oo-oo whoo-oo-oo… "

You can act this out with your hands. Build the house by placing clenched fists on top of each other; raise arms above the head with fingers touching for the roof; straighten the arms for the chimney — and hoot loudly for the wind.

## Once I Caught a Fish Alive

" One, two, three, four, five,

Once I caught a fish alive.

Six, seven, eight, nine, ten,

Then I let it go again.

Why did you let it go?

Because it bit my finger so.

Which finger did it bite?

This little finger on the right. "

## One, Two, Three, Four

" One, two, three, four,

Mary at the cottage door,

Five, six, seven, eight,

Eating cherries off a plate. "

You might vary this for individual children:
"One, two, three, four; Martin at the nursery door, Five, six, seven, eight; Eating popcorn off a plate."

## Five Currant Buns

" Five currant buns in a baker's shop,

Round and fat with sugar on the top.

Along came a girl with a penny one day,

Bought a currant bun and took it right away.

Four currant buns, *and so on…* "

You can act this out out with five children pretending to be buns, and another child being the person who buys one. Or children can use their fingers to count as they sing.

## One, Two, Buckle My Shoe

" One, two, buckle my shoe;

Three, four, knock at the door;

Five, six, pick up sticks;

Seven, eight, lay them straight;

Nine, ten, big fat hen;

Eleven, twelve, dig and delve;

Thirteen, fourteen, maids a-courting;

Fifteen, sixteen, maids in the kitchen;

Seventeen, eighteen, maids in waiting;

Nineteen, twenty, my plate's empty. "

## Six Little Snails

" Six little snails,

Lived in a tree.

The wind blew hard

And down came three.

*How many were left?*

Three little snails

Lived in a tree.

The wind blew hard

And down came three

*How many were left?* "

The chidren can show numbers with their fingers. You can make up variations. For example: 'Ten little snails lived in a shoe, The wind blew hard and out came two.'

## Useful tips

 Children can use their fingers to show which number they are up to.

 With subtraction songs, such as 'Six Little Snails', children show the number with their fingers. They can bend down the number of fingers they need to subtract. Ask "How many are left?"

 Instead of saying the numbers, point to them on a number line and let the children say them for you.

 You can use props such as pictures of currant buns, or toy currant buns, to make the rhyme real.

 Children can hold up number cards to show the numbers.

# Cooking

" let children do as
much as they can
for themselves "

## The recipe

Whatever recipe you use, the questions to ask children and the things to notice about what they do will be similar. It is important to let children do as much as they can for themselves. Young children will spill ingredients. They will pile flour on to the balance, and then see that they have to take lots off again. They will over- and under-estimate quantities in surprising ways. But it is vital that they do all this themselves so that they can learn from experience.

The task for older children is to read the recipe themselves and do the cooking on their own. You can check from time to time by asking them questions about what they have to do next. An extra challenge for older children is to ask them to increase the quantities in the recipe to make enough for two groups or the whole class.

## The mathematics in cooking

Mostly, cooking involves measuring:

| | |
|---|---|
| **weight** | using a balance with weights one side, or kitchen scales |
| **capacity** | using a measuring jug or measuring spoons |
| **time** | using a clock or a kitchen timer |

Sometimes cooking involves counting. Children need to read numbers on weights, scales and jugs. If you ask children to double or treble the recipe they have to calculate the new quantities.

We ask young children to weigh things using a balance. This is difficult because the arms of the balance have to be level. Often young children don't have the experience to know how to do this. They keep piling things on one side when they should be taking them off, so the balance stays firmly down on one side. It takes a lot of patience to watch them and let them do it, before they finally realise what they have to do.

When children use kitchen scales, they often need help in reading the dials. You can point out the range of numbers, and ask children to work out

what numbers the markers in between stand for. You will also need to help children with measuring jugs and spoons. If children haven't yet done much work with weighing scales or measuring jugs it may be best just to tell them where the right mark is. You could explain what the numbers mean.

A kitchen timer is very useful to show children how to measure the passing of time. The timer shows you at any point how much longer you have to wait. You can use this alongside a classroom clock, and compare the two. For example, you could say: "How many more minutes will the buns take to cook? Seven? Look at the clock — when will seven minutes be up? What time will that be?"

You can ask young children questions about how many rolls or cakes they are making. You can ask how many they have made so far, and how many more they need to make. You can get them to arrange the buns in rows so that they can see the pattern of the number. You can encourage them to count in twos or threes, and to show you half the buns on the tray.

# Soda Bread Buns

## Ingredients for 12 buns

150 g plain white flour

150 g wholemeal flour

40 g butter

200–300 ml milk

2 teaspoons baking powder

1 heaped teaspoon sugar

a large pinch of salt

a squeeze of lemon juice

## To serve

Butter, sliced banana, cottage cheese…

## The method

◆ Preheat the oven to 190°C (gas mark 5).

◆ Sift the dry ingredients together into a large bowl.

◆ Rub in the butter.

◆ Add the lemon juice and mix in enough milk to make a soft dough — don't let the dough get too wet.

◆ Divide the dough into 12 portions and shape each portion into a roll — don't handle the dough too much. Leave the buns with a rough finish.

◆ Place the buns on a greased baking sheet.

◆ Dust them with a little flour and make a small cross in the top.

◆ Bake them for 10–15 minutes — don't allow them to go too brown.

## Questions to ask

➜ Which of the weights do you need to weigh out 150 g of flour?

➜ Where on the scale is the 150 g mark? How can you tell?

➜ Where on this jug is 200 ml? How can you tell?

➜ What does 'heaped teaspoon' mean?

➜ Are all the rolls exactly the same size?

➜ How many rolls have you made? How many more do you need to make twelve?

➜ At what time will the rolls be ready to take out of the oven?

➜ How long should we set the timer for?

## Things to notice

### Can the children…

➜ follow a recipe?

➜ weigh out the ingredients accurately using a balance of some sort?

➜ read the dial of the kitchen scales accurately?

➜ read a capacity container accurately?

➜ work out the passing of time?

➜ work out the approximate amount of ingredients they need for 24 or 36 rolls (or six rolls)?

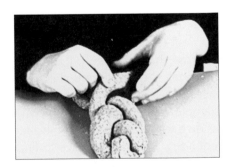

67

**Cooking**

# The Home Corner

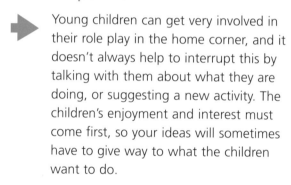

The home corner is an area that you can adapt for all kinds of role play. Sometimes the home corner is a pretend home, and at other times you can make it into a hospital or a shop or an aeroplane, and so on. Whatever is going on in the home corner, there is plenty of scope for mathematics.

The home corner is most useful in helping children with their social and language skills. Young children get very absorbed in their play and it doesn't always help to stop their game by asking them to count the cups or to tell you which doll is the biggest. The mathematics learning must fit into the children's imaginary games.

Sometimes you can join in with children in their games by taking part in their fantasy. You can then ask questions to make children think, such as: "The teddies and I would all like a cup of tea too. Are there enough cups?" or "Panda wants to go to sleep too. Is there a bed big enough for him?".

It works well to set up an activity away from the home corner that is linked to it, and which has a mathematical theme. Often children will take these ideas back to the home corner in their play. For example, you could put out dolls and dolls' clothes on a table. The dolls and the clothes are all different sizes. The children have to find the right clothes for each doll. Or you could set up a telephone kiosk. Children could invent numbers and make a telephone book. When you put these activities back into the home corner, children will often merge them into their own games.

## Useful tips

➤ Young children can get very involved in their role play in the home corner, and it doesn't always help to interrupt this by talking with them about what they are doing, or suggesting a new activity. The children's enjoyment and interest must come first, so your ideas will sometimes have to give way to what the children want to do.

➤ Try observing for a while, then entering the game by taking on a role yourself.

➤ Set up an activity while the children are still on the mat with the teacher, and invite some of them to join in.

## Train, shop, hospital, café. . .

You can turn the home corner into a place of work, such as a train, a shop, a hospital, a café, and so on. This gives scope for counting and using money, as well as reading and writing numbers.

*15   16   17   18   19   20   21   22*

## What children can do

◆ Count out coins to pay the shopkeeper or ticket collector.

◆ Make a time for their appointment and draw a clock to show that time.

◆ Make travel tickets with you, showing the price and the seat number.

◆ Write menus and price lists.

◆ Make price labels to stick on the goods for sale.

◆ Weigh their luggage on bathroom scales.

◆ Take each other's temperature and write it down.

◆ Put out the seats for the train and number each one.

## Questions to ask

➡ How many people can go on the train?

➡ How much does it cost to go to London?

➡ What time is your appointment?

➡ How much does your suitcase weigh?

➡ How many people are waiting to see the doctor?

➡ What number is your seat on the train?

➡ How high is her temperature?

## Having a picnic

There is lots of mathematics in real or imaginary meals, parties and picnics.

### What children can do

- Lay places for everybody there.
- Put a 'teabag' in each mug.
- Put a cherry on each cake.
- Share out the biscuits fairly.
- Cut the sandwiches exactly in half. How many pieces are there now? What if these pieces were cut in half again?
- Choose a bottle that they think holds enough juice for four people — and then check if it does.
- Compare two jugs to see which holds more.

### Questions to ask

- → How many buns are there? Are there enough for everybody?
- → Which jug would you use? Why would you use that one?
- → How can we check whether that is the best one to use?
- → Which jug holds more?
- → Can you give the biggest bun to the biggest teddy?

## Washing up

When the children wash plates or equipment with you, they get experience in counting and in comparing the sizes of things.

### What children can do

- Count how many Duplo pieces they have washed.
- Count how many dirty plates there are in the pile.
- Sort the things that have been washed up and put them away.
- Arrange the clean pots in order of size.

### Questions to ask

- → How many mugs can we fit in the bowl?
- → Will the forks fit in this box?
- → Can you count how many spoons there are here?
- → Are there more dirty blocks or clean ones?

# Out and About

## On an outing

1 2 3 4 5 6 7 8 9 10 11 12 13 14

### In the playground

When you are out and about with children — in the playground or on an outing — you can use mathematical language and ideas. Children are naturally interested in the everyday world, so you can supply them with facts and ideas to think about.

> How many paving stones can you jump?

> What time does the clock say?

> Which is taller, the bus stop or the house?

## Useful tips

➤ Help children learn how to tell the time. One child can keep an eye on the time (either their own watch or a school clock) and tell you when playtime is over.

➤ Each day choose a different theme to interest the children. For example, during playtime encourage the children to count hops, skips and jumps.

71

# On an outing

## Just talking

◆ Discuss the route to the shop, the school garden or the main entrance.

◆ Is the road straight or curved?

◆ Is the ground bumpy or flat?

◆ Do we turn left at the corner, or do we go straight on?

## Counting

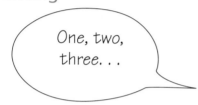

One, two, three. . .

◆ Count children, swings, tyres, dogs, lamp posts or trees. Discuss whether there are more trees or lamp posts.

◆ Count the tricycles. How many wheels on a tricycle? On two tricycles? On three?

◆ Count the pushchairs. How many wheels on a pushchair? On two pushchairs? On three?

◆ Do all the windows have the same number of panes?

◆ How many window panes are there in that window? And in that one?

◆ How many strides does it take to get to the climbing frame or the steps or the shop? Are child strides and adult strides the same size? Are Judy's strides the same size as Frank's?

## Numbers

◆ Look for numbers on doors.

◆ What do the children notice about the door numbers in a street? Why do the numbers go 1, 3, 5, 7...?

◆ Look for numbers on buses, in shop windows, on posters or street signs.

◆ Who can find a sign with their age in it?

◆ Read out the numbers on the car number plate.

## M894 CLM

◆ Who can find a number plate with the number 3 in it?

◆ Which number in the number plate is the biggest?

## Time

◆ What time does the clock say? Is it right? See if the children can tell the time — if not, read them the time yourself.

◆ Discuss what sort of display the clock has. Is it analogue (with hands) or digital (with just numbers)?

◆ What sort of numerals does the clock have? Does it have special computer numerals made up of lighted bars, or Arabic numerals (1, 2, 3 and so on), or Roman numerals (I, II, III, IV, V and so on)?

◆ If the numerals are Roman, what do these different numbers mean?

## Patterns

◆ Look for patterns in brickwork, fences or paving stones. How would you make these patterns yourself?

◆ Look for patterns in fabric in shops. Can you see where the pattern repeats?

◆ Look for patterns in the way tins are arranged on the shelf. Why don't these tins fall down?

## Post boxes

◆ Find out who can reach the letter slot.

◆ Look to see how many times the post van collects letters each day. Is it the same every day?

◆ At what times are the collections made? Can the children say the times in two ways, for example '3:45' and 'a quarter to 4'?

◆ Discuss which is taller, the post box or the wall.

## Bus stops

◆ Which buses go from this stop?

◆ What does the timetable tell us?

## Opening times

◆ Shops, doctors, swimming pools and so on often display their opening times on a notice outside their door. Look to see what time they open and close.

| OPENING TIMES | |
| --- | --- |
| Monday – Friday | 8am to 8pm |
| Saturday | 8am to 6pm |
| Sunday | Closed |

◆ Work out how many hours they are open.

◆ Find out whether they close at all during the day and, if so, for how long.

## Positions

◆ Talk about what is next to the shop.

◆ Ask what is between the post office and the greengrocers.

◆ Try to remember which is the first shop we come to, and the next one…

◆ Talk about what is under or behind or over or in front of the tree.

## Collections

◆ Collect conkers, acorns and fir cones to use as counting materials back at school.

◆ Collect feathers and conkers for weighing.

◆ Keep bus and train tickets to look at the numbers and see what they mean.

73

# In the playground

In this section you will find games and activities involving mathematics which you can help children organise in the playground.

How many steps can you do?

## About the games and activities

On the next few pages there are games and activities for three different age groups. However, you could try the games with children of other ages and see what appeals to the children. Sometimes you may be supervising a lot of children outside. In this case, you will want to teach a group of children a game and then leave them to play by themselves. Sometimes you can work with another adult and take turns playing with a small group of children, and taking responsibility for the rest of the group.

*27 28 29 30 31 32 33 34 35 36 37 38 39 40*

# Counting hops, skips and jumps

Children need to practise counting. Activities they enjoy give them a purpose for counting.

Children might use:

- skipping ropes
- sand-timers
- skittles
- balls
- beanbags
- hoops

## Things to notice

Can children count…

➜ How many times they can hop, jump or skip without stopping?

➜ How many hops, jumps or skips they can do before the sand in the timer has run through?

➜ How many times in a minute they can throw a beanbag at a skittle or into a hoop?

➜ How many times they can throw and catch a ball without dropping it, either on their own or in pairs?

*One, two three, four, five. . .*

## Questions to ask

➜ What number comes next?

➜ How many skips did you do? How many do you think you'll be able to do next time?

➜ How many hops can you do along this line?

➜ What number do you get to if you skip across the playground, counting your skips?

➜ Can you do 100 throws? It doesn't matter if you stop — you can carry on counting without starting at 1 again.

➜ Who did the most hops?

➜ Which of your legs can you hop on for the longest?

➜ How many skips do you think you could do in half a minute?

➜ How many more hops would you have to do to reach 20?

➜ How many more jumps did you do this time?

In the playground

# Playground activity

## Using playground markings

Many playgrounds are painted with grids, ladders or other shapes. Sometimes numbers are painted on the playground. You can use these markings for all sorts of mathematics. Sometimes you may need to improvise.

Forward 2 and right 3. . .

## Number track

### The children can

♦ Walk along the track, saying each number as they step on to it.

♦ Find a number with a six in it.

♦ Stand on a number so as to hide it and challenge a friend to say what the hidden number is.

♦ Run along the lines clockwise, then stop and go anti-clockwise.

### Questions to ask

➜ Walk along the track, saying the numbers… Now stop and close your eyes. Can you tell me the next few numbers?

➜ Stand beside me and close your eyes. Can you point to where the 10 is?

➜ How many right hand turns do you need to get back to where the line starts?

*19 20 21 22 23 24 25 26 27 28 29 30 31 32 33 34 35 36 37 38*

### 100-Grid

## The children can

- Use a giant dice, and stones instead of counters, to play a 'track' game where they race each other from 1 to 100.

- Start on 1 and jump on every other square, saying the numbers they land on.

- Start on 2 and jump on every other square, saying the numbers they land on.

- Work out how many jumps of two they need to make to get to 10.

- Count in threes, and put a skittle on every third number. What is the pattern?

- Count in fives, or twos, and look for the pattern.

## Questions to ask

→ Throw some beanbags onto the grid. Now tell me: how many must you count on from the red beanbag to get to the blue beanbag?

→ How many would you need to count on from the yellow beanbag to get to a tens number?

### Copy cat

## How to play

- Two children join together to make a shape with their bodies.

- The rest of the children get into pairs and copy the shape.

## Questions to ask

→ What does that shape look like?

→ How could you make a letter or number with your bodies?

→ Pretend you are a mirror. Face your partner and copy their movements.

# Playground activity

## Giant strides

### What the children do

◆ Draw a line for children to stand on, and a second line some distance away across the playground (or use the playground markings if they are already there). Ask the children how far they think it is from one line to the other in giant strides.

◆ They then test out their estimates.

### Questions to ask

➜ Who took the fewest strides?

➜ How many more strides did you take than Nasrul?

➜ Mina took 23 strides. Do you still think your guess of 50 strides is a good one, or would you like to change it?

➜ How many strides will it take you to take to get there and back?

➜ How many strides will it take if you go there and Alan comes back?

➜ Is your giant stride longer than a metre? Is it shorter than a metre?

## Timing

### The children can

- Count in tens, and see how far they can count in a minute.
- Time a friend as they run right round the playground.
- Check how many times their friend's heart beats in a minute — before and after exercise.

### Questions to ask

→ You ran round faster than Jasmin, but did you run as far? Was it fair?

15 16 17 18 19 20 21 22 23 24 25 26 27 28 29 30 31 32 33

## Estimating

### The children can

- Work out how many bricks there are in the wall.
- Estimate how many children there are in the playground.
- Guess how tall the school is in metres.

### Questions to ask

→ How might you work that out?

→ How many bricks are there in a row?

→ About how many rows are there?

How many bricks?

**In the playground**

# Useful Information

# Mathematical Equipment

There is usually a lot of equipment in the classroom to help children understand mathematics. It isn't always obvious what each piece of equipment is for. Even when it's easy to see what it is for, you may not know how to use it to help children learn. In this section we talk about the equipment you are most likely to come across and how you can use it.

16  17  18  19  20

# Number

## Abacus

The beads on the abacus are used to show numbers. There is one spike for hundreds, one for tens, and so on. You can read the number by counting the number of beads on each spike. An abacus is useful to support understanding of place value (see Glossary, p86) and fractions and decimals.

## Base 10 blocks

Often called Dienes or Multibase blocks. The blocks are either wooden or plastic. They have small cubes known as 'units' or 'ones', 'longs', which are ten units long, 'flats', which are ten longs wide and 'blocks', which are ten flats high. The blocks are used to help children understand place value (see Glossary, p86).

## Calculators

Children need to know quite a lot of mathematics to use a calculator properly. They have to decide what kind of calculation they are doing, and which buttons to press. If they press the wrong button, and get a wrong answer, they should be able to spot this and start again. The calculator should not be used to avoid learning number facts. Children need to know their number facts and be able to calculate in their heads. Calculators are best used in the later primary years.

> How many minutes have you been alive?…

> First I need to work out how many minutes in a day; that's 60 × 24, so I must press 60 × 24 =

## Cards

Number cards are useful for many games and activities. The cards may go from 0 to 9, or from 0 to 100.

You can also use ordinary playing cards for number activities.

## Coloured rods

Cuisenaire and Colour Factor are the most common types of coloured rods. These are wooden rods of different lengths representing numbers 1 to 10 (Cuisenaire) or 1 to 12 (Colour Factor). You can use the rods for addition, subtraction, multiplication and division as well as fractions.

## Counters

Counters, conkers, fircones, beads, straws and buttons are all good for counting.

## Cubes

 You can join Unifix cubes together to make sticks of various lengths. Unifix cubes are useful for counting, place value work (see Glossary, p86) and block graphs.

 You can join Multilink together on all sides. Multilink cubes are useful in the same way as Unifix. They are also useful for work on volume and shape.

 Centicubes are 1 cm wide, long and high. You can join them together in any direction. They are useful for work on capacity as well as number. Each centicube weighs 1 gram.

## Dice

You can find everyday 1–6 dice in most classrooms. You can use them for countless games and mental mathematics activities. You can also get dice of different shapes with four faces, eight faces, twelve faces and twenty faces. Blank dice are useful because you can write on them any numbers you choose.

## Dominoes

You can use dominoes with younger children for counting and matching, and with older children for all kinds of number puzzles. You can get dominoes up to double nine, as well as the more usual double six.

## Number lines

Number lines help children to build up an image of numbers in order, and help them learn to count forwards and backwards. You can use number lines for multiplication, division and number patterns. You can also get blank number lines, which you can use to help children with larger numbers, fractions or decimals.

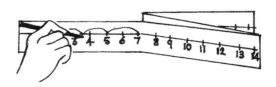

## Capacity

### Measuring jugs

You can get measuring jugs of different capacities, such as one litre, two litre or ½ litre.

Jugs and cylinders are calibrated in different ways. Children need to learn how to use these calibrations.

## Money

### Coins and notes

In some classrooms, children use toy coins and notes, while in others they use real coins. Using coins in mathematical activities helps children learn about how the money system works.

## Length

### Rulers and metre rules

Rulers and metre rules are marked in different ways. They may be marked in blocks of ten centimetres, in centimetres and half centimetres, or in centimetres and millimetres. Children need to learn that they must start with the 0 point when measuring length, which is not necessarily at the beginning of the ruler.

### Surveyor's tape

These are usually 10 m or 20 m long. They are marked in metres and decimals of a metre. The markings can be difficult to understand, so you may find them more suitable for use with older children.

### Tape measures

Tape measures are useful for measuring curved objects, or things measuring more than a metre. If one side is marked in feet and inches and the other in centimetres, make sure that children are using the correct side.

### Trundle wheels

A trundle wheel measures distance along the ground. One rotation of the wheel equals one metre. Children enjoy pushing these around, but they usually find it difficult to understand how they work until they older.

## Measuring angles

### Protractors, angle indicators and rotograms

These are all used for measuring angles. An angle is an amount of turn and is measured in degrees. For example a full turn is 360° a quarter turn or right angle is 90°.

## Weight

### Balances

Balances compare the weights of two objects. You can also use weights on one side to balance an object.

### Weighing scales

Like old-fashioned kitchen scales, weighing scales have a pan on one side and a platform for weights on the other. They work in the same way as a balance. Use metric weights (grams and kilograms), not pounds and ounces.

### Dial scales (bathroom and kitchen scales)

Children can find dials difficult to read. Don't use dial scales until the children have had experience of balances. Again, use metric units (grams and kilograms), not pounds and ounces.

**Mathematical Equipment**

### Spring balances

The more something weighs, the more the spring is pulled down. Some spring balances are used to measure forces in science and are calibrated in Newtons. Others show grams and kilograms. Again, you will need to explain to children how to read the calibrations.

# Time

### Sand timers

These are just like old-fashioned egg-timers. Use them to measure specific lengths of time, such as three minutes.

### Digital clocks

Children need to learn how to read digital clocks as well as the traditional ('analogue') type of clock face.

### Geared clocks

A geared clock is more realistic than a card clock face, as the hands move together like a real clock. You could also use an old household clock.

### Kitchen timers

Use a kitchen timer to measure a specific length of time. The timer will ring when the set time is up. This is useful for giving children a sense of how long a minute, five minutes or half an hour is.

### Stop clocks and watches

These measure time very accurately. Use them with older children to compare running speeds.

# Temperature

### Thermometers

Make sure the children are using thermometers that are calibrated in Celsius (also known as centigrade), rather than Fahrenheit. You can use thermometers for science as well as mathematics.

# 2D and 3D shape

### 2D shapes

2D or flat shapes are used for activities such as sorting and pattern making. They are useful for getting to know the names of shapes and what they are like. For example, squares fit together with no gaps and circles don't.

### 3D shapes

3D shapes or solids are used in activities such as sorting. Again, these are useful for getting to know about names and properties of solids. For example, cubes have six sides ('faces'), all of which are square.

# Glossary

**Analogue**

Analogue clocks and watches show the time using hour and minute (and sometimes second) hands.

**Bar chart**

A bar chart is often used in primary schools to display information about numbers of people or things — for example, the numbers of children who voted for different names for the new guinea pig.

**Capacity**

The capacity of a container is the amount of space inside it.

**Centimetre**

A centimetre is shorter than half an inch. There are 100 centimetres in a metre.

**Data, data-handling**

Data is another word for information. When children work at data-handling, they collect information then organise and display it in some way. The children might collect data about people's heart rates, or running speeds.

**Difference**

The difference between two numbers is how much bigger one is than the other. If Sammi has five marbles and Jo has nine, the difference is four — in other words, Jo has four more than Sammi. You can find the difference by subtracting one number from the other.

**Digit**

All numbers are made up using the digits 0, 1, 2, 3, 4, 5, 6, 7, 8, 9. Two-digit numbers, such as 56, have two digits; three-digit numbers, such as 398, have three; one-digit numbers such as 7 or 3 have one.

**Digital**

Digital watches show the time in the form of digits.

**Even**

The even numbers (2, 4, 6, 8 and so on) can all be divided exactly in two.

**Factor**

When a number is broken up into smaller numbers by division, these smaller numbers are called factors. For example, 30 can be broken up into two of its factors, 5 and 6, because $5 \times 6 = 30$. 3 and 10 are also factors of 30, because $3 \times 10 = 30$. So are 15 and 2, because $15 \times 2 = 30$.

**Metre**

A metre is just over a yard, or 3 feet. There are 100 centimetres in a metre.

**Model**

A model of something shows its essential character, but is not an exact replica. A scale model of a house shows the shape exactly as it is, but much smaller, and may not bother about details such as showing each brick. You can use an abacus to model numbers in much the same way. An abacus shows the essential facts about the number — how many hundreds, tens and units it contains — but does not tell you whether the number is odd or even, or if it can be divided by 5.

**Multiple**

If you multiply 9 by other numbers, the results are all multiples of 9. So, for example, 18, 27, 90 and 99 are all multiples of 9.

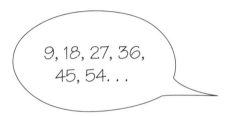

9, 18, 27, 36, 45, 54. . .

**Multiplication tables**

Some children learn their multiplication tables by chanting. Other children learn the multiplication facts a few at a time, perhaps by looking at the number patterns in the tables. How they learn does not matter, as long as they do learn the multiplication facts.

**Negative numbers**

Numbers less than zero are called negative numbers.

-6 -5 -4 -3 -2 -1 0 1 2 3 4 5 6 7 8 9 10 and so on.

**Net**

When you unfold a box and lay it flat, you are making the net of the box. Children often explore different nets that can all be folded up to make a cube.

**Number bonds**

The number bonds or number facts are the basic facts about number which children need to learn by heart. Important addition and subtraction bonds include $2 + 2 = 4$, $2 + 3 = 5$, $8 - 6 = 2$, $8 - 7 = 1$. The important multiplication and division facts are all in the multiplication tables.

**Number line**

A number line is a useful way of modelling numbers. Number lines start from 0, not 1. Children can work out addition and subtraction problems by drawing steps and jumps from one number to another. Older children can look at the spaces between the numbers. They can talk about the decimal or fraction numbers that belong in those spaces.

## Number tracks

Number tracks are useful for young children, and appear in games such as Snakes and Ladders. Children can move counters along them, and begin to learn how many steps it takes to get from one number to another.

## Odd

Odd numbers (1, 3, 5, 7 and so on) are numbers which you cannot divide exactly by two.

Half of 7 is 3 with 1 left over

## Operations

$+$ $-$ $\div$ $\times$

There are four main number operations: addition, subtraction, multiplication and division. When you start with a number such as 59 and add or subtract something from it, you are operating on the number 59.

## Place value

In any number over 9, the digits have different values depending on their position, or place, in the number. So, for example, in the number 749, the seven is worth 700, but in 73, the seven is worth 70. This is called place value.

## Plenary

The plenary comes at the end of a class lesson, and generally takes about ten minutes. It gives children a chance to present their work to others, and talk about each others work. It helps the teacher to assess how children have done and pinp[oint areas where further work is needed.

## Product

When you multiply two numbers together the result is called the product. The product of 3 and 4 is 12.

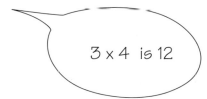

3 x 4 is 12

## Quotient

The quotient is the answer to a division problem. For example, if 20 is divided by 5, the quotient is 4.

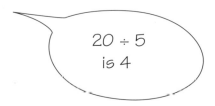

20 ÷ 5 is 4

## Remainder

What is 'left over' when doing a division problem. For example, if 21 is divided by 5, the answer is 4, remainder 1. This could be written: 21 ÷ 5 = 4r1.

## Subtract

Subtraction is a general word that covers both 'take away' and 'difference'. If Sammi has nine marbles and loses five, a subtraction or take away calculation will tell us that Sammi has four left. If Jo has nine marbles and Sammi has five, the difference is four: Jo has four more than Sammi. These two situations are quite different. In the first situation, only one person has marbles. In the second situation, both people have marbles. But both these situations can be written out as the same subtraction calculation, 9 − 5 = 4.

## Sum

In ordinary speech, a 'sum' can be an addition, a subtraction, a multiplication or a division. But in mathematics the term 'sum' should strictly be used only for additions, because it actually means 'total'. So the sum of 5 and 9 is 14.

## Unit

Unit means one. It describes numbers under 10 as in the phrase 'hundreds, tens and units'. Units are also used in measuring. When we measure weight or length, we use units which are all the same size such as inches, centimetres or grams. You can put these units together to make larger units (for example, 12 inches to the foot, or 1000 grams to the kilogram).

# Mathematical Targets

" what most children should
be able to do at the end
of Years 1, 2, 3, 4, 5 and 6 "

3 4 5 6 7 8 9 10 11 12 13
2
1

This section shows some of the key things that children of different ages should know at the end of each year. It is likely that you will work with some children who can't do everything on the list for their age group. But it is important to know what we expect of children and to try to help them achieve it.

89

# By the end of **Year 1** most children

should be able to...
- say the numbers in order to at least 100
- count 20 or more objects
- count in ones and tens
- read and write numbers to at least 20
- add and subtract numbers to ten in their heads
- know by heart pairs of numbers that make ten, for example 6 + 4
- work out how many wheels there are on three bikes
- work out simple doubles of numbers to 10
- recognise coins and work out how to make 14p with three coins
- read the time to the hour or half hour on a clockface

# By the end of **Year 2** most children

should be able to...
- count and read numbers to at least 100
- count up to 100 objects in groups of 10
- count in twos, fives and tens
- say the number ten more or ten less than any number up to 100
- add and subtract numbers to twenty in their heads
- know by heart pairs of 'tens' numbers that make 100, such as 30 + 70
- work out simple multiplication such as 5 times 2
- work out simple division such as 6 divided by 2
- work out doubles and halves such as double 35 and half of 18
- solve problems with money, such as finding ways of spending 50p using silver coins
- read the time to the half and quarter hour

1 2 3 4 5 6

# By the end of **Year 3** most children

should be able to...
- count, read and write numbers to 1000
- count in twos, threes, fours, fives, tens and hundreds
- say the number one hundred more or one hundred less than any number up to 100
- add several small numbers, such as 4 + 7 + 2 + 3
- know by heart addition and subtraction facts for all numbers up to 20
- work out multiplication such as 5 times 8
- work out division such as 25 divided by 5
- work out doubles and halves such as double 19 and half of 150
- solve problems with money, such as finding five coins to make 74p
- read the time to the nearest five minutes

# By the end of **Year 4** most children

should be able to...
- count, read and write numbers up to 10 000
- add or subtract 1, 10, 100 or 1000 from any whole number up to 10 000
- add and subtract numbers to 100 in their heads
- multiply or divide whole numbers by 10 or 100 in their heads
- say a number that is, say, half way between 740 and 750
- recognise numbers in the 2, 3, 4, 5 and 10 times tables
- mentally add and subtract numbers such as 79 + 58 and 63 + 46
- know pairs of numbers that make 100, such as 66 + 34
- quickly work out multiplications such as 12 times 4
- quickly work out divisions such as 69 divided by 3
- work out, say, 41 ÷ 4 as 10 remainder 1
- know by heart doubles of all numbers 1 to 50
- solve problems with money, such as buying three different things and working out change for £10
- use a TV guide to work out how long the programmes last
- use a ruler to draw and measure lines to the nearest centimetre

**Mathematical Targets**

# By the end of **Year 5** most children

should be able to... 
- count, read and write numbers to one million
- multiply or divide whole numbers by 10, 100 and 1000
- say a number that is, say, half way between 27,400 and 28,000
- recognise numbers in the 6, 7, 8, 9 and 11 times tables
- mentally add and subtract numbers such as 3754 plus 30 and 127 minus 35
- know pairs of decimals that make one, for example 0·7 + 0·3
- work out quickly multiplication such as 7 times 8
- work out quickly division such as 56 divided by 7
- work out, say 43 ÷ 9 as 4 remainder 7
- double all numbers from 1 to 100
- solve problems with money, such as finding change from £20 for £13·68
- use a train timetable
- work out the perimeter and area of a rectangle

# By the end of **Year 6** most children

should be able to...
- count, read and write any numbers
- multiply or divide numbers, including decimals, by 10, 100 and 1000
- say a number that is, say, half way between -80 and +20
- recognise large numbers that are multiples of 2, 3, 4, and so on
- add and subtract numbers such as 4250 + 3536 and 750 − 2551
- know pairs of decimals that make one, for example 0·71 + 0·29
- work out quickly multiplication such as 9 times 8
- work out quickly division such as 112 divided by 7
- work out, say, 63 ÷ 8 as 7·875
- solve problems with money, such as sharing £363 630 among three people, or the sale price of some £30 jeans with 10% off
- work out different times around the world
- use a ruler to draw lines and measure to the nearest millimetre
- use a protractor to measure angles up to 90 degrees

1 2 3 4 5 6 7 8 9 10

# Feedback Sheet

A feedback sheet is a useful way for the adults in a busy classroom to communicate

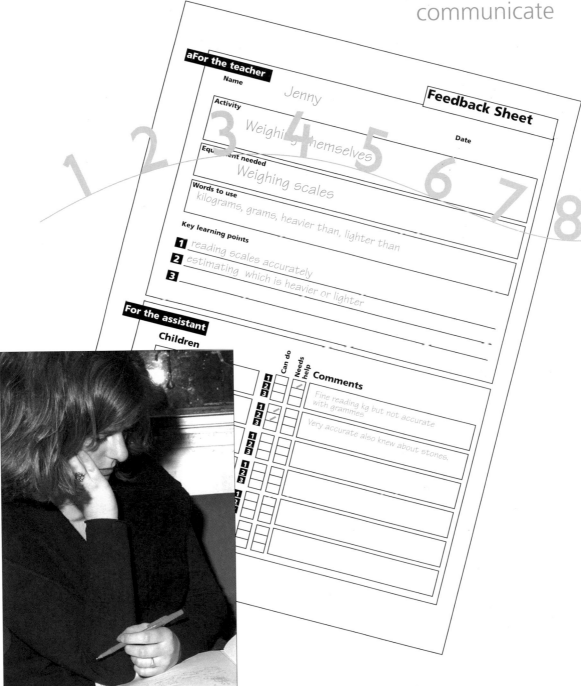

**aFor the teacher**

Name

Jenny

**Feedback Sheet**

Activity

Weighing themselves

Date

Equipment needed

Weighing scales

Words to use

kilograms, grams, heavier than, lighter than

Key learning points

1 reading scales accurately

2 estimating which is heavier or lighter

3

**For the assistant**

Children

| | Can do | Needs help | Comments |
|---|---|---|---|
| 1 2 3 | | ✓ | |
| 1 2 3 | ✓ | | Fine reading kg but not accurate with grammes |
| 1 2 3 | | | Very accurate also knew about stones. |
| 1 2 3 | | | |
| 1 2 3 | | | |
| 1 | | | |

Classroom assistants are often asked to support a child, or a group of children, with a mathematics task set by the teacher. A feedback sheet is a useful way for the adults in a busy classroom to communicate, since finding a chance to talk can be difficult. On page 95 you will find a sample feedback sheet, which you can change to suit your school's own needs.

# How to use the Feedback Sheet

## Before the lesson

The teacher fills in:

**Activity**        what the activity involves

**Equipment needed**     what equipment will be needed

**Words to use**     any specific mathematical vocabulary
that the assistant should use and
encourage the children to use

**Key learning points**     up to three things that the teacher
particularly wants the assistant to
look out for (for example: 'does
the child add numbers mentally?
does the child read the weighing
scales dial correctly?')

The assistant:

- reads what the teacher has planned
- checks that the equipment is available

## During the lesson

The assistant:

- discusses with the children what they are doing
- asks open questions to prompt children's thinking and encourage them to demonstrate what they know and understand
- asks closed questions, in order to find out what facts children know
- ticks the appropriate box to show success at one of the 'Key learning points'.
- comments on anything else that would interest the teacher

## After the lesson

The assistant:

- discusses with the children what they have learnt

# Feedback Sheet

## For the teacher

**Name**                                                    **Date**

**Activity**

**Equipment needed**

**Words to use**

**Key learning points**

**1** _____

**2** _____

**3** _____

## For the assistant

| Children | | Can do | Needs help | Comments |
|---|---|---|---|---|
| | **1** **2** **3** | | | |
| | **1** **2** **3** | | | |
| | **1** **2** **3** | | | |
| | **1** **2** **3** | | | |
| | **1** **2** **3** | | | |
| | **1** **2** **3** | | | |

Feedback

# Other Resources

### Board Games for the Nursery

**Carole Skinner and Fran Mosley**
**BEAM**
**ISBN 18 74099 75 8**

There are five games in the set, all on A2 laminated card. The games use everyday objects such as conkers, cubes and simple dice. The games deal with aspects of counting, and each one has an easy version suitable for nursery children, as well as a 'harder' version for children in the Reception class. The supporting notes explain how to play the games, and suggest variations.

### Board Games for Key Stage 1

**Fran Mosley**
**BEAM**
**ISBN 18 74099 86 3**

There are four full-colour board games in the set, all on A3 laminated card: 'Snake Pits', 'Slippery Slope', 'Trains' and 'Land on a Number'. They deal with mental addition and subtraction, and are suitable for children at KS1 and those at KS2 who may need more practice with number. The supporting notes explain how to play the games and suggest variations.

### Jills of All Trades: Classroom Assistants in KS1 classes

**Janet Moyles and Wendy Suschitzky**
**Association of Teachers and Lecturers,**
**7 Northumberland Street, London WC2N 5DA**
**Tel 0171 930 6441**

This book is the result of a 16-month investigation into the roles and relationships of KS1 teachers and the classroom assistants they work with, including those training as Specialist Teacher Assistants. It outlines existing practice in primary schools and makes recommendations for future development. A summary of the research and recommendations is also available.

### Learning Mathematics in the Nursery: Desirable Approaches

**The Early Childhood Mathematics Group**
**BEAM**
**ISBN 18 74099 63 4**

This award-winning book outlines the mathematics children should experience before they start compulsory schooling: in nurseries, playgroups and as four-year-olds in reception classes. Sections include: mathematical language, recognising patterns, counting, larger numbers, reading numbers and mathematics through rhymes, songs and stories. Each section looks at the mathematics involved and the development of children's understanding in this area, then gives ideas about what to provide, things to discuss with children and what to look for in children's talk and behaviour that will show you what they do and don't understand.

### Help in the Classroom: A Practical Guide to Making the Most of Non-teaching Assistants

**Margaret H Balshaw**
**David Fulton Publishers**
**ISBN 18 53461 32 6**

This book provides practical advice to help your school make the most of its classroom assistants. It looks at the issues surrounding the employment and training of non-teaching staff, and suggests ways to examine and develop school policies. The book is aimed at coordinators and those responsible for in service training, rather than classroom assistants themselves.

### Maths Games Books

**Calculators in Their Hands**
**BEAM**
**ISBN 18 74099 38 3**

**Cards on the Table**
**BEAM**
**ISBN 18 74099 13 8**

**Numbers in Your Head**
**BEAM**
**ISBN 18 74099 73 1**

**Casting the Dice**
**BEAM**
**ISDN 10 74099 83 9**

A collection of mathematical games using everyday items such as calculators, playing cards, dice, paper and pencils. The books can be used in the classroom, given out as homework or simply enjoyed by children on their own. Suitable for children aged 8 to 14.

### Big 100-Grid

**BEAM**

Useful for a variety of games and activities with children of any age. Numbered on one side, with a blank grid on the other. The grid is varnished so that it can be written on with felt-tipped pen and then wiped clean again. Comes with a free water-based pen.

### Number Cards

**BEAM**

A pack of ten A4 sheets, each containing two sets of 0–9 number cards. Children should ideally be supplied with two complete sets of cards each. Useful for a wide range of mathematical games and activities.

## Acknowledgements

**BEAM would like to thank the following for their help in the development of this book:**

Rob Briscoe
Sheila Ebbutt
Ros Elphinstone
Sarah Gale
Ian Grant
Anne Kennelly
Fran Mosley
Barbara Newmarch
Billie Old
Anita Straker

Hasan Chawdhry and Wilberforce Primary School, Westminster
Sandra Roberts and Shapla Primary School, Tower Hamlets
Henrietta Harrison and Smithy Street Primary School, Tower Hamlets
Jackie Trudgeon and Canon Barnett Primary School, Tower Hamlets
Sue Walsh and Ben Jonson Primary School, Tower Hamlets

The learning support assistants in Tower Hamlets who commented on and trialled **Assisting Numeracy**

Members of the Islington Schools Development Group

Photographs:
Special thanks to Ben Jonson Primary School, Tower Hamlets